How this curriculum is designed

This curriculum is designed to guide you through a sequence of scenarios that relate to a common topic in mathematics. As you progress through the scenarios, use the approach listed below.

Step 1: Try. Do the scenario on your own.

Step 2: Check. Look at the answer key. It may match or relate to your result. It may teach you something new. It may show you that you need guidance from someone else.

Step 3: Edit. Find and fix your mistakes if you can. Seek guidance, if needed.

After Step 3, advance to the next scenario and do Step 1 again.

Advice from students who have used this curriculum

"The answer key is there to help you. Use it."
"Check the answer key after every scenario."
"Try to find connections between different scenarios."
"Focus on each scenario and try to understand how it connects to the main topic."
"Read the explanations between problems or sets of problems because everything is connected and the information will still apply in 2 problems or 20 problems."
"If you have a question, go back to previous scenarios because there are steps that build up to where you are."

Contents

Introduction to intersecting lines

Using equations to find the intersection point

The Substitution Method

The Elimination Method

When two lines do not intersect at a single point

Scenarios that involve systems of equations

Systems of linear inequalities

Additional scenarios

Introduction to intersecting lines

1. A boy gets up early one morning to go for a long ride on his bicycle. Thirty-six minutes later, his older sister realizes he left the inhaler that he uses for his asthma, so she gets in the car and tries to catch him.

   Use the graph to estimate what time it is when the older sister catches her brother.

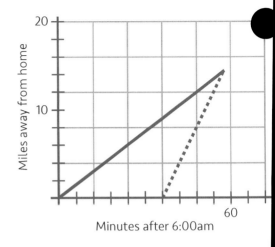

Looking at the graph, it seems impossible to determine the exact time at which the sister catches up with her brother because the grid lines (which help you determine exact numbers) do not line up nicely at the point where the dashed line intersects the path of the solid line.

When you first started graphing points on a Cartesian plane, you learned that there is information contained in each point. Similarly, since lines can be used to represent meaningful values, the intersection of two lines can also contain information.

2. Without using specific numbers, describe the information that is contained in the intersection point of the two lines in the scenario above.

In one sense, because you can see the point of intersection, the information that is contained in that point is directly in front of you. For now, though, you can probably only *estimate* where the two lines intersect. In the scenarios that follow, you will gradually discover how to calculate the exact coordinates of the point where two lines intersect.

3. You will eventually learn how to find the exact time that the sister catches her brother, but first, consider a simpler example. Looking at the graph shown, where do the two solid lines intersect?

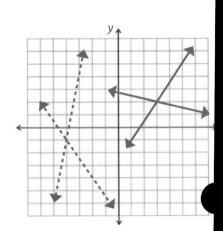

4. Where do the two dashed lines intersect?

5. Your cousin has been working at a company for several months when you join his sales team. At first, you make fewer sales each month than your cousin. Over time, though, you realize you are catching up to him.

a. How long after you join the sales team will you match your cousin's total monthly sales? Assume you both keep increasing your monthly sales at constant rates.

b. By what amount do your total sales increase each month?

c. What are your total monthly sales during the month that you catch your cousin?

6. To refresh your familiarity with graphing lines, prove that the following lines intersect at (−2, −5) by graphing them.

Equation 1: $y = 3x + 1$

Equation 2: $y = -\frac{1}{2}x - 6$

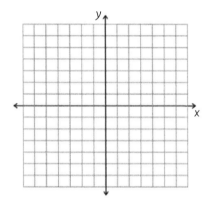

In a previous lesson, you learned how to determine the equation of a line when you can see its graph. However, even though you were comfortable with this at one point, it may be buried in your memories right now. Venture back into this topic by working through the next scenario.

7. Although there are various forms that you can use when you write the equation of a line, like Standard Form and Point-Slope Form, write your equation in Slope-Intercept Form for now. What is the Slope-Intercept Form for the equation of a line?

8. Determine the equation of each line shown.

a.

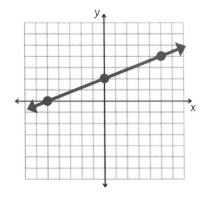

b.

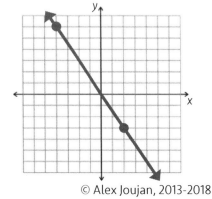

9. Determine the equation of each line shown.

a.

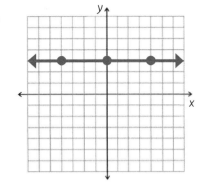

b.

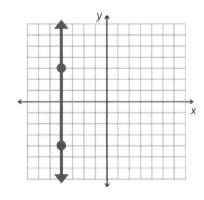

10. It will be helpful later on to make sure that you are familiar with replacing variables in equations with specific numbers. Consider the equation $y = 2x + 1$.

    a. If the value of x is 0, then the value of y is $2(0)+1$, or ____ .

    b. If the value of x is 1, then y is ____ .

    c. If x is 2, then $y =$ ____ .

    ★d. If $y = 2$, then $x =$ ____ .

11. Now consider the equation $y = \frac{1}{4}x + 2$.

    a. What is the value of y if $x = 4$?   b. What is the value of x if $y = -2$?

    ★c. What is the y-value if $x = \frac{1}{2}$? Write the result as a fraction and as a decimal.

12. For the equation $y = -\frac{2}{3}x - 4$, what is the value of y if $x = -\frac{9}{4}$?

13. ★For the equation $y = -\dfrac{4}{5}x + 1$, what is the value of y if $x = 3\dfrac{3}{4}$?

14. Each equation below is written in Standard Form, $Ax + By = C$. Rearrange the equation to write it in Slope-Intercept Form, $y = mx + b$.

     a. $3x + y = 7$ b. $3x - y = 7$

15. Rearrange the equation to write it in Slope-Intercept Form.

     $4x - 5y = 10$

16. Is the slope of the line shown positive or negative?

    a. 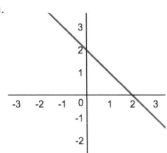   b. 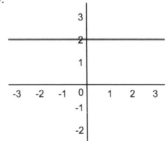   c.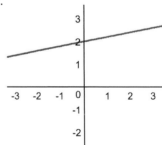

Notes

Using equations to find the intersection point

17. You are now ready to get back to the topic of intersecting lines. In the graph to the right, where do the two lines intersect?

    Do not spend much time on this. Instead, estimate the location.

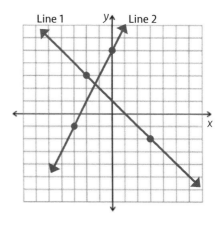

18. Once again, like the scenario about the older sister and her brother, you cannot accurately determine the intersection point. It is close to (−1, 2), but something in your brain tells you that there are fractions contained in those coordinates. Both lines have dots marked on them to highlight locations where the coordinates <u>are</u> integers. Use points on each line to write the equations of Line 1 and Line 2.

19. Now that you have the equations, consider this: each line is a set of points...infinitely many points. Since the lines are separate, they do not share the same points. For example...

    a. If an ant is walking along Line 1 and it stops when it lands on a point with an x-value of 1, what is the y-value at that point?

    b. If that same ant is walking along Line 2 and it stops on a point with an x-value of 1, what is the y-value at that point?

    c. What are the y-values of Lines 1 and 2 when x = −2?

    d. What are the x-values of Lines 1 and 2 when y = −1?

    You could answer questions like these over and over again and you would find that each time you select the same x-value for Lines 1 and 2, the y-values are different. Similarly, if you pick a single y-value for Lines 1 and 2, the x-values will be different. However, there is ONE x-value where both lines have the SAME y-value. This is where the lines intersect.

20. Since the equation for Line 1 is y = −x + 1, you could write it as y_1 = −x + 1 (the "1" in y_1 shows that this equation is for Line _____).

21. Since the equation for Line 2 is y = 2x + 5, you could write it as y_2 = 2x + 5 (the "2" in y_2 shows that this equation is for Line _____).

When you look for the point where Lines 1 and 2 intersect, you are trying to find a single point where the y-value for Line 1 is the same as the y-value for Line 2. In other words, you want to find the point on the graph where $y_1 = y_2$. Since $y_1 = -x + 1$ and $y_2 = 2x + 5$, you can replace y_1 and y_2 with the expressions that they equal. This makes a new statement: $-x + 1 = 2x + 5$.

22. You may realize at this point that you have a question you can answer. Use your algebra skills to solve the equation $-x + 1 = 2x + 5$.

23. Your calculations should reveal that Line 1 and Line 2 have the same y-value when $x = -\dfrac{4}{3}$. Confirm that both lines actually have the same y-value when $x = -\dfrac{4}{3}$.

 a. For Line 1, if $x = -\dfrac{4}{3}$ and $y_1 = -x + 1$, then $y_1 = -\left(-\dfrac{4}{3}\right) + 1$. After simplifying, $y_1 =$ _____.

 b. For Line 2, if $x = -\dfrac{4}{3}$ and $y_2 = 2x + 5$, then $y_2 = 2\left(-\dfrac{4}{3}\right) + 5$. After simplifying, $y_2 =$ _____.

24. Now that you have done these calculations, look at the graph of the two lines one more time. Where do the lines intersect? Use your work in the previous scenario to answer this question. Write the intersection as an ordered pair.

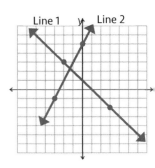

25. Did you follow the logical progression of the previous scenarios? Try another one on your own. Without graphing, determine the intersection point of the graphs of $y = 2x - 7$ and $y = -4x + 5$.

26. Without graphing, determine the intersection point of the two lines.

     a. $y = x - 8$ and $y = -5x + 10$ ★b. $y = \dfrac{1}{5}x + 3$ and $y = -3x + 11$

27. Before you become convinced that these equations will always be in Slope-Intercept Form, where do the graphs of $6x - 2y = 22$ and $y + 4x = 10$ intersect?

28. ★Where do the graphs of $3x - 2y = 8$ and $3x = -4y + 20$ intersect?

29. Write the equation of the line shown in the graph. Use the Slope-Intercept Form of a linear equation. Check the graph to confirm the accuracy of your equation.

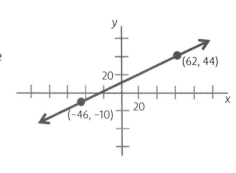

30. Determine the intersection point of the two lines shown.

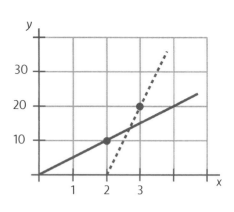

31. ★Go back to scenario 1 and determine the exact time when the sister catches her brother.

The Substitution Method

You are now familiar with <u>one</u> method for determining the intersection point of two lines. The next method that you learn will use what you have learned in previous lessons about replacing a variable with another value.

32. Start with the equation $y = 2x + 7$.

  a. What is the value of y if x is replaced with 5?

  b. Rewrite the equation if $x = 10$.

  c. Rewrite the equation if $x = 2M$.

  d. Rewrite the equation if x is replaced with "$f + 1$".

  e. Rewrite the equation if x is replaced with "$5 - 3y$".

33. Now start with the equation $2x - 4y = 12$.

  a. Rewrite the equation if x is replaced with "$y + 2$".

  b. Rewrite the equation if $x = 3y - 2$.

  c. Rewrite the equation if y is replaced with "$2x - 9$".

  d. Rewrite the equation if $y = -4x - 3$".

34. In the equation $2x - 4y = 12$, there are two variables, x and y. In the previous scenario, when one of the variables is replaced with another expression, the resulting equation contains only one variable. Solve each of these resulting equations.

35. Consider Line 1, $y = -2x + 3$, and Line 2, $-6x + 2y = -14$. Graph them in the Cartesian plane provided.

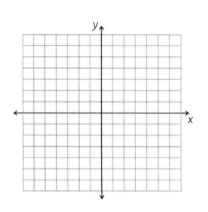

Notice the point where the two lines intersect. At this point, the y-values are the same. In other words, the y-value for $y = -2x + 3$ is the same as the y-value for $-6x + 2y = -14$. Since the y-values are the same, and y equals $-2x + 3$, then the y-value in $-6x + 2y = -14$ also equals $-2x + 3$.

36. In the equation $-6x + 2y = -14$, replace the y with $-2x + 3$. An equation with two variables now contains only one variable. Solve this equation.

37. Your calculations in the previous scenario reveal that the lines intersect when $x = 2$. Since both lines pass through that intersection point, they will both have the same y-value when you replace x with 2 in each equation. Show this by replacing x with 2 in each equation and solving for y both times.

38. The method you just used is called the Substitution Method because you use an expression $(-2x + 3)$ as a substitute for another variable (y). This method shows that the line $-6x + 2y = -14$ and the line $y = -2x + 3$ intersect at the point (___, ___).

39. Consider another pair of equations: $2x + 3y = -1$ and $x = 5y + 6$. In the equation $2x + 3y = -1$, replace the x-value with the <u>other</u> expression that x is "equal to" $(5y + 6)$. Now that the equation only contains the variable y, solve for y.

40. Finish the work you started in the previous scenario to find the intersection point of the lines $2x + 3y = -1$ and $x = 5y + 6$.

As you can see from your work, the Substitution Method allows you to find the exact point where two lines intersect. It does not matter which variable you choose for the substitution.

41. Find the point where the two lines $y=-6x+2$ and $-4x+3y=-16$ intersect. Do this by substituting the first equation into the second equation.

42. Find the point where the two lines $4x-7y=10$ and $x=\frac{1}{2}y-5$ intersect. Do this by substituting the second equation into the first equation.

43. Determine the intersection point of each pair of lines using the Substitution Method.

a. $\begin{array}{l} 5x+2y=19 \\ y=3x-7 \end{array}$

b. $\begin{array}{l} x-6y=10 \\ x=10-2y \end{array}$

44. Determine the intersection point of each pair of lines using the Substitution Method.

a. $\begin{array}{l} 6y-3x=-9 \\ y=2x+6 \end{array}$

b. $\begin{array}{l} 4y-20=x \\ -2x+3y=-15 \end{array}$

45. Use the Substitution Method to find the intersection point of the lines shown.

$$2x + y = 6$$
$$3y - 4x = 8$$

46. Two lines are given below. Where do they intersect?

Line 1: $y = 2x - 2$ Line 2: $3y + 2x = 9$

47. ★Two lines are shown in the graph. The equation of the line with the positive slope is shown below. Where do the lines intersect?

$$-5x + 6y = 30$$

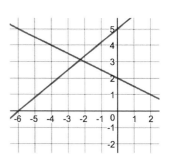

48. Where on the graph do the two lines intersect?

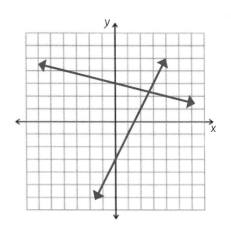

Notes

The Elimination Method

Now that you have gained familiarity with the Substitution Method, you will learn about one more method for finding the intersection point of two lines. This next method combines basic arithmetic (addition, subtraction, etc...) with a clever bit of logic.

49. Consider the following scenarios. In each scenario, you are given two complete equations. Use those equations to determine the missing information in the incomplete third equation.

   a. If $6x = A$ and $7x = B$, then $13x =$ _____.

   b. If $10y = A$ and $-3y = B$, then _____ $= A + B$.

   c. If $A = 2x + 3y$ and $B = 5x - y$, then $A + B =$ _____.

   d. If $x - 2y = 100$ and $7x + 2y = 200$, then _____ $= 300$.

50. Fill in the missing information in the third equation.

   a. If $5x + 3y = 12$ and $2x + 6y = 7$, then $7x + 9y =$ _____.

   b. If $-3x + 2y = 9$ and $5x - 6y = -4$, then $2x - 4y =$ _____.

   c. If $3x + 4y = 1$ and $5x + y = 4$, then $13x + 6y =$ _____.

51. Fill in the missing expression to make each addition scenario true.

   a. $\dfrac{\begin{array}{cc} 2x & 5y \\ + \underline{} & + \underline{} \end{array}}{\begin{array}{cc} 7x & 8y \end{array}}$

   b. $\dfrac{\begin{array}{l} 3x + 2y = 7 \\ + \underline{} \end{array}}{8x + 0y = 3}$

   c. $\dfrac{\begin{array}{l} -2x + 6y = 10 \\ + \underline{} \end{array}}{x + 0y = 13}$

52. Fill in the missing equation to make each subtraction scenario true.

   a. $\dfrac{\begin{array}{l} 7x + 8y = 7 \\ - \underline{} \end{array}}{2x + 5y = 3}$

   b. $\dfrac{\begin{array}{l} 4x + y = 9 \\ - \underline{} \end{array}}{0x + 2y = 3}$

   c. $\dfrac{\begin{array}{l} -6x + 4y = 5 \\ - \underline{} \end{array}}{x + 0y = 8}$

53. Since subtracting can be challenging at times, scenarios will focus only on adding equations for now. Combine each pair of equations by adding downward. This will create a new equation.

   a. $\dfrac{\begin{array}{l} -2x + 4y = 15 \\ +\quad 2x + 6y = 5 \end{array}}{}$

   b. $\dfrac{\begin{array}{l} x + 3y = 60 \\ +\quad 7x - 3y = 20 \end{array}}{}$

   c. $\dfrac{\begin{array}{l} 5x + 2y = 12 \\ +\quad -5x - 3y = -9 \end{array}}{}$

Now that you have completed the mental exercises in the previous two scenarios, you will see how adding and subtracting equations can be used to find where two lines intersect.

54. Consider two equations: $4x + 7y = 17$ and $-4x + 2y = 10$.

If $4x + 7y = 17$ and $-4x + 2y = 10$, then _____ = 27.

55. Look at the previous scenario another way. Line up the equations to write one above the other.

$4x + 7y = 17$
$-4x + 2y = 10$

Now complete the following operations. In part a. below, combine the two equations by adding downward. In part b. below, combine the two equations by subtracting downward.

a. ADD
$4x + 7y = 17$
$-4x + 2y = 10$

b. SUBTRACT (be careful!)
$4x + 7y = 17$
$-4x + 2y = 10$

56. When you subtract the two equations in the previous scenario, the resulting equation is still a two-variable equation ($8x + 5y = 7$), so it remains unsolvable. However, when you add the two equations, the resulting equation is $9y = 27$. You can solve this equation to show that $y = 3$.

a. One of the original equations was $4x + 7y = 17$. Let $y = 3$ in this equation. Solve for x.

b. The other original equation was $-4x + 2y = 10$. Let $y = 3$ in this equation and solve for x.

c. Explain the significance of what you find.

57. Combine each pair of equations by adding downward. This will create a new equation.

a.
$-x + 3y = 7$
$x + 2y = 3$

b.
$7x + 4y = 12$
$5x - 4y = 36$

c.
$-4x + 3y = 9$
$2x + 6y = -12$

58. As you can see in the previous scenario, when you have two equations with two variables and you combine the equations by adding downward, one of the variables may be eliminated, although in part c., this does not happen. This elimination is helpful because it converts a pair of 2-variable equations into a single 1-variable equation.

    a. Finish what you started in part a. in the previous scenario. Find the coordinates of the point where the lines $-x + 3y = 7$ and $x + 2y = 3$ intersect.

    b. Now finish part b. in the previous scenario. Find the coordinates of the point where the line $7x + 4y = 12$ intersects the line $5x - 4y = 36$.

    c. In the previous scenario, why is it that in part c., neither variable is eliminated by addition?

In part c., when you add the two equations, you need to change a coefficient in one of the equations to eliminate a variable. It would be easy if you could just change a number that you see and replace it with one that you want. In a sense, you can do that, as long as you are careful about how you do it.

59. You can change an equation by multiplying both sides by the same number. Use this principle to fill in the blanks in each statement below.

    a. $2x + 3y = 5$ is the same equation as $8x + 12y =$ _____.

    b. $-x + 6y = 12$ is the same equation as _____$x + 18y = 36$.

    c. $12x + 4y = 20$ is the same equation as $6x + 2y =$ _____.

60. Fill in the blanks in each statement below.

    a. $-3x + 7y = 12$ is the same equation as _____$x - 21y =$ _____.

    b. $9x - 2y = -10$ is the same equation as _____$x +$ _____$y = 40$.

61. In a previous scenario, you combined the equations below by adding downward. This created a new equation, but it did not eliminate one of the variables. Change the appearance of one of the equations below to make addition eliminate one of the variables. Change one of the equations, but do not add the equations together.

$$-4x + 3y = 9$$
$$2x + 6y = -12$$

19

© Alex Joujan, 2013-2018

62. Now that you have changed one of the previous equations, find the intersection point of the lines formed by those two equations.

63. Find the intersection point of the graphs of 5x + 2y = 2 and 4x + y = −2 by lining up the equations and using addition to eliminate one of the variables.

64. Earlier, you learned how to find the intersection point of two lines by replacing a variable with an expression that is "equal" to that variable. This is called the _____ Method.

65. You have now seen another strategy for finding the intersection of two lines. This new strategy involves adding two equations in order to eliminate one of the variables and it is known as (surprise!) the _____ Method.

66. If you choose to use the Elimination Method, it is helpful to rewrite the equations in Standard Form (Ax + By = C). Consider the following pairs of equations.

Group A:
$$2y = 10 + 7x$$
$$-7x = 9y - 12$$

Group B:
$$-7x + 2y = 10$$
$$7x + 9y = 12$$

Which group is easier to work with if you use the Elimination Method? Explain your choice.

67. The intersection point of each pair of equations shown below can be found using the Elimination Method, but the order of one of the equations in each pair needs to be changed to make it easy to combine the equations. Rewrite one of the equations to put both equations in Standard Form, but **do not** do any further calculations.

a.
$$-2x - 5y = -2$$
$$4 = 2x + 6y$$

b.
$$2x + 5y = 2$$
$$2 - x = 3y$$

c.
$$3y = -x + 2$$
$$4x + 10y = 4$$

68. Find the intersection point of each pair of lines using the Elimination Method.

a.
$$-x+3y=7$$
$$x+2y=3$$

b.
$$7x+4y=12$$
$$5x-4y=36$$

69. Find the intersection point of the lines shown using the Elimination Method.

$$-10x+4y=28$$
$$2x-8y=16$$

70. Instead of adding, can you subtract two equations to eliminate a variable? Explain your reasoning.

71. Why is it usually easier to do the Elimination Method by adding two equations?

72. Find the intersection point of each pair of lines using the Elimination Method.

a.
$$6y-3x=-9$$
$$y=2x+6$$

★b.
$$y=\frac{1}{4}x+20$$
$$-2x+3y=-15$$

73. Find the intersection point of the pair of lines using the Elimination Method.

$$3x-9y=-18$$
$$5y-2x=4$$

74. ★Two lines are represented by the equations $9x - 4y = 14$ and $2x + 3y = -28$. Find the intersection point using the method stated below.

      a. Elimination Method   b. Substitution Method

75. ★At what location on the graph do the two lines intersect?

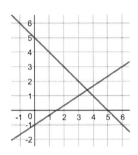

76. At what location on the graph do the two lines intersect?

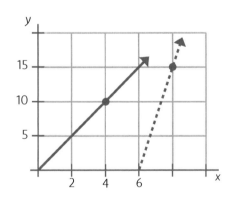

77. Will two lines always intersect at a single point? Can you think of a situation where this would not happen?

Notes

When two lines do not intersect at a single point

78. This may seem like review, but solve the equations shown below.

    a. $2+5y=5y-4$ b. $10-2y=-2\left(y-3\right)+4$

79. Two lines are shown. Where do the lines intersect?

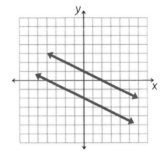

80. Graph the two lines shown below. Using the graph, where do the lines intersect?

$$y=\frac{2}{3}x-3 \text{ and } y=\frac{2}{3}x+1$$

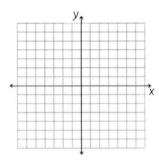

81. Without graphing (use either Substitution or Elimination), determine the intersection point of the graphs of $y=3x-5$ and $3x-y=-1$. Graph the lines to check your work.

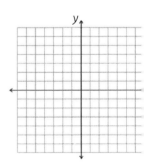

82. Use either Substitution or Elimination to determine the intersection point of the graphs of $y=\frac{1}{2}x+6$ and $2x=4y-24$. Graph the lines to check your work.

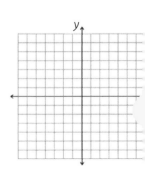

83. Determine the intersection point of each pair of lines without graphing. Use any method.

a.
$$2x+y=3$$
$$6x+3y=9$$

b.
$$4x-8y=3$$
$$-3x+6y=-3$$

Let's review what you have been learning. Using algebraic methods, you can locate the exact intersection point of two lines. The intersection point has two values, x and y, a horizontal position and a vertical position. Think about what happens if the lines do not intersect at a single point.

84. When two lines never intersect, they are _____ _____. You can use algebraic methods to find the intersection point, but your calculations will create a false statement, such as 0 = 3, or 7 = 8. The false statement occurs because no intersection point exists.

85. When two equations represent _____ _____ _____, you can use algebraic methods to find the intersection point, but your calculations will produce a statement that is always true, such as 0 = 0, or 5 = 5. The true statement occurs because when two lines are actually _____ _____ _____, they will always intersect, everywhere, infinitely many times.

86. Use the logic in the previous two paragraphs to take another look at The Substitution Method. Consider the two equations shown. Do not do any calculations. Keep reading below them.

Equation 1: $3x+y=6$
Equation 2: $x+2y=10$

Ignore Equation 2 and focus only on Equation 1.

a. Isolate the variable y in Equation 1.

b. Use your resulting equation from part a. to make a substitution for y in Equation 1. Plug your equation, $y=-3x+6$, into Equation 1, but not into Equation 2. Solve this resulting 1-variable equation.

87. Consider the equations below one more time.

Equation 1: $3x + y = 6$

Equation 2: $x + 2y = 10$

This time, ignore Equation 1 and focus only on Equation 2.

a. Isolate the variable x in Equation 2.

b. Use your resulting equation from part a. to make a substitution for x in <u>Equation 2</u>. Plug your equation $x = -2y + 10$ into Equation 2, but not into Equation 1. Solve this resulting 1-variable equation.

Notes

Scenarios that involve systems of equations

Each scenario so far has involved the intersection point of two lines. Since a line is a collection of points, with each point containing 2 pieces of information (an x-value and y-value), the methods for finding these x- and y-values can be used for any scenario that involves two related quantities. Use what you have learned so far to work through each of the following scenarios.

You have solved systems equations containing only x's and y's. If these variables are changed to other letters, it may seem confusing at first, but it does not change anything about what you have learned.

88. Use the **substitution** method to find the values of w and E that make both equations true.

$$E = \frac{1}{2}w - 7$$
$$4w + 2E = 26$$

89. Use the **substitution** method to find the values of m and K that make both equations true.

$$K = 150 - 12m$$
$$K = 130 - 9.5m$$

90. Use the **elimination** method to find the values of f and g that make both equations true.

$$1.25f + 5.25g = 10.50$$
$$f + g = 18$$

91. On May 1, 2014, the toll rate for passing through the Holland Tunnel into New York City was $13 for a car and $22 for a bus. Suppose a total of 3,000 cars and buses passed through the tunnel in one hour, and a total of $46,290 in tolls was collected.

    a. Write an equation that relates the number of cars, c, and the number of buses, b, to the total number of cars and buses that passed through the tunnel in one hour.

    b. Write an equation that shows the relationship between c and b and the total amount of money collected in tolls.

    c. How many cars and how many buses passed through the tunnel during that hour?

92. Drew is doing a temperature experiment. He fills a pot with cold water and places it over a fire to make the water get hotter. He fills another pot with hot water and puts that pot in a freezer to make that water get colder. As the temperatures in the pots change, they follow linear patterns, which are modeled by the equations $T=-5m+180$ and $T=4m+36$. In both equations, T represents the temperature, in Fahrenheit, m minutes after Drew starts recording the temperatures.

    a. What is the temperature of the hot water at the moment Drew starts recording its temperature?

    b. After how many minutes will the water in the two pots be the same temperature?

    c. What is the temperature of the water in the pots when their temperatures are the same?

93. A creamery sells ice cream and limits the options to make the lines move quickly. Customers can order one scoop of ice cream for $1.99 or two scoops for $2.99 and the ice cream is always served on a waffle cone. One summer day, the creamery sold 348 cones and their revenue totaled $889.52.

    a. Write an equation that relates the number of single scoop cones, s, and the number of double scoop cones, d, to the total number of cones that were purchased.

    b. Write an equation that shows that relationship between s and d and the total revenue.

    c. How many single scoop ice cream cones did the creamery sell?

94. A rectangle has a length L and a width W.

    a. If the perimeter of the rectangle is 12 cm, write an equation that shows the relationship between L, W, and the perimeter.

    b. If the perimeter of the rectangle is 12 cm, and the length is 2 cm more than the width, what are the dimensions of the rectangle?

95. Suppose a used Honda Civic costs $11,000 if you buy it today and it will lose $800 in resale value every year. Suppose a used Ford Focus costs $14,000 if you buy it today and its resale value will decline by $1,200 every year.

   a. Write an equation that relates the resale value, V, of a Honda Civic to the number of years, y, that have passed since you bought it.

   b. Write an equation that relates the resale value, V, of a Ford Focus to the number of years, y, that have passed since you bought it.

   c. Which car will have the higher resale value after 4 years?

   d. How long would you need to own the Civic before its resale value is the same as the resale value of the Focus?

96. During his record-setting season in 1998, an NFL placekicker named Gary Anderson became the first kicker to complete a perfect regular season. He had 94 total kick attempts, and he scored a total of 164 points that season. If a kick can be worth either 1 point for a Point After Touchdown (PAT), or 3 points for a field goal, how many field goals did Gary make in 1998?

97. In a jar on your desk, you have a collection of dimes and quarters. Instead of counting them by yourself, you bring the coins to a bank. After the coins are counted, you find out that there were 788 coins. The total value of the coins is $117.80. How many coins of each type did you have in the jar?

98. Rewrite the previous scenario about the coins to match the system of equations shown below.

   Equation 1: $N + D = 517$
   Equation 2: $0.05N + 0.1D = 41.60$

99. ★The Stellar Cellular Co. charges $80 per month with an extra charge of $0.20 per text message after you send 500 text messages. The Cell Allure Phone Co. charges $70 per month with an extra charge of $0.24 per text message after you send 500 messages.

    a. If you send 600 text messages one month, which company's plan would you want?

    b. How many text messages would you need to send in one month in order for both plans to have the same total cost?

100. A fisherman in Alaska catches fish all morning and then takes them to a market to sell them. At one market, a fisherman sells king crab for $5 per pound and salmon for $3.50 per pound. He sells a total of 128 pounds of crab and salmon and he earns $499. How many pounds of king crab and how many pounds of salmon did he sell?

101. Rewrite the previous scenario about the fisherman to match the system of equations shown below.

    Equation 1: $9.2C + 6S = 605$
    Equation 2: $C + S = 85$

102. ★A pipe is turned on and begins filling a tank with water. After two and a half minutes, another pipe is turned on and begins filling another tank with water. Both pipes are turned off when the tanks contain the same amount of water.

    a. For how many minutes was the second pipe turned on?

    b. How much water is in each tank when both of the pipes are turned off?

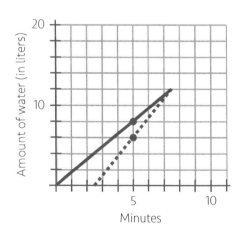

    c. Identify the equations of the two lines in the graph.

Notes

Systems of linear inequalities

Many of the scenarios so far have focused on finding the point at which two quantities are equal.

> When are the temperatures the same? When do the cars have equal resale values? When will the tanks contain the same amount of water? After how many text messages will the phone plan costs be identical?

Working through these scenarios involves analyzing the relationships between two quantities.

> The temperature is related to the current time. The value of a laptop changes with respect to its age. The amount of water in a tank depends on how long a pipe has been turned on. The cost of a phone plan increases with the number of text messages.

In mathematics, relationships between quantities can often be represented by equations. When multiple equations are combined to determine unknown values, the collection of these equations is often referred to as a system of equations. You have now learned how to use the Substitution Method and the Elimination Method to determine when the variables in two equations represent the same values. This is known as solving a system of equations.

Although many of the previous scenarios have involved equality, which shows up as a single location on the Cartesian plane or a single number for the value of a variable, these scenarios can be altered to involve **in**equality. In a previous lesson, you learned how to graph a linear inequality.

103. In the Cartesian plane shown, plot all of the ordered pairs that have an x-value of 3. How many points can you find?

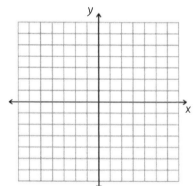

104. In the same plane to the right, graph all of the ordered pairs that have an x-value that is less than 3. How many points can you find?

When you combine the points that lie along the vertical line in your graph above with the points that occupy the space to the left of the vertical line, these points form the solution of the inequality $x \leq 3$. A common way to show this solution on a graph is to draw the vertical line for $x = 3$ and darken the region to the left of the line. The darkened region contains all of the ordered pairs with x-values less than or equal to 3.

105. In the Cartesian plane shown, plot all of the ordered pairs that have a y-value of –2.

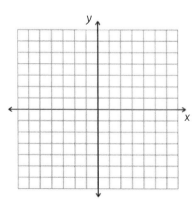

106. In the same plane shown to the right, graph all of the ordered pairs that have a y-value that is greater than –2.

107. When you combine the points on the horizontal line in the previous graph and the points that occupy the space above the horizontal line, these points form the solution of the inequality $y \geq -2$. How can you change the graph in the previous scenario to display the solution region for the inequality $y > -2$?

108. Graph each inequality.

a. $x > -4$

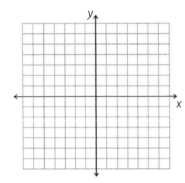

b. $y < 1$

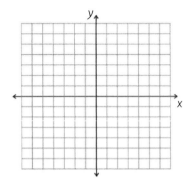

109. Graph each inequality.

a. $x \leq 5$

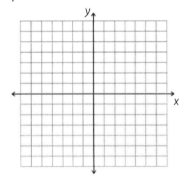

b. $y \geq 4$

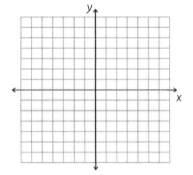

110. Circle the inequalities that would have a shaded region that includes the boundary line.

a. $y < x - 3$ b. $y \leq 1 - 3x$ c. $y + x > 6$ d. $2x - 5y \leq 10$

111. Graph the two equations shown below.

a. $y = -2x + 5$

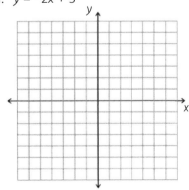

b. $3x - 4y = 12$

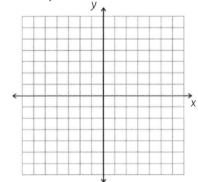

112. Isolate the variable y in the inequality below.

    a. $2x + y > 5$ b. $3x - 4y < 12$

113. In the Cartesian plane shown, plot all of the ordered pairs that satisfy the relationship below.

      The y-value is 1 more than the x-value.

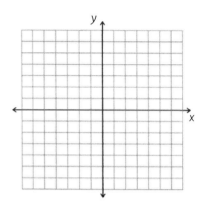

114. The points that you plotted to the right should form a line that can be represented by the equation $y = x + 1$. In the same plane shown to the right, plot all of the ordered pairs that satisfy the relationship $y > x + 1$.

In the previous scenario, when you combine the points <u>on</u> the slanted line in your graph and the points that are <u>above</u> that line, these points form the solution of the inequality $y \geq x + 1$.

115. Match each inequality with its graph.

    a. $y > -\dfrac{1}{4}x + 2$ b. $y \geq -2$ c. $y \leq x - 3$ d. $x < -3$

i.
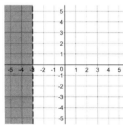

ii.
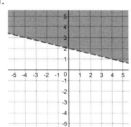

iii.
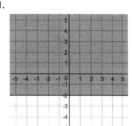

iv.
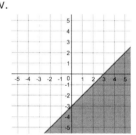

116. Graph the two inequalities shown below.

    a. $y < x - 3$ b. $2x - 5y \leq 10$

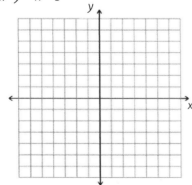

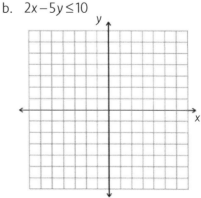

35

117. Is the ordered pair (0, 0) part of the solution region in either graph in the previous scenario?

118. Write the inequality that has the shaded solution region shown in each graph below.

a.

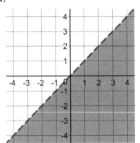

b.

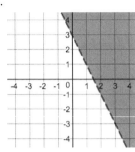

c.

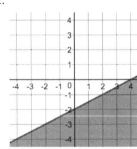

119. Now consider an inequality that has 2 restrictions. In the graph to the right, plot as many points as you can that satisfy the conditions below.

The x-value is greater than 1.

The y-value is greater than 3.

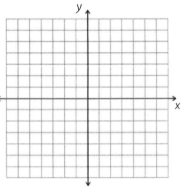

120. The lines in the graph shown divide the plane into 4 regions. Shade in the region that satisfies the 2 inequalities below.

$x \leq -2$
$y \geq -1$

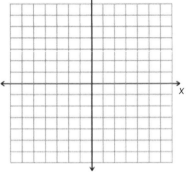

121. The lines in the graph shown divide the plane into 4 regions. Shade in the region that satisfies the 2 inequalities below.

$y \geq x - 3$
$y \leq -x + 2$

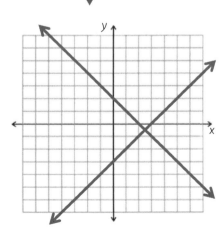

122. How would you change the graph in the previous scenario to display the solution region if the inequalities were changed to become $y > x - 3$ and $y < -x + 2$?

When you graph a linear inequality, the darkened (or shaded) region displays the ordered pairs that make the inequality true. When you graph two linear inequalities, the shaded region displays the ordered pairs that make both inequalities true.

123. Display the solution of the system of inequalities. This is also known as graphing the system.

$$y \geq \frac{1}{2}x - 4$$
$$y < -2x + 1$$

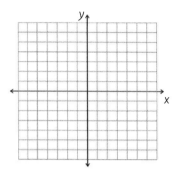

124. Graph the system of inequalities.

$$x + y \leq 4$$
$$x - y < 4$$

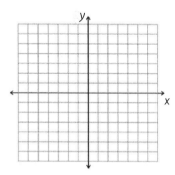

125. Graph the system of inequalities.

$$y < 2$$
$$x \geq -3$$
$$x - 3y < 6$$

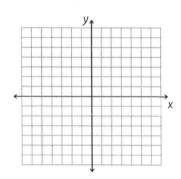

126. Calculate the area of the triangular shaded region in the previous scenario.

Notes

127. Consider the following graph.

    a. During what year will the laptops have the same resale value?

    b. In 2015, what will be the difference between the resale values of the two laptops?

    c. Express the rate at which each laptop loses it value, in dollars per year.

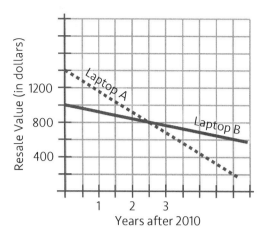

128. ★A pipe is opened and it begins filling Tank A with water. After three minutes, another pipe is opened and it begins filling Tank B with water.

    a. Circle the region in the graph that represents when Tank B contains more water than Tank A.

    b. After 8 minutes, how many more liters of water will there be in Tank B than in Tank A?

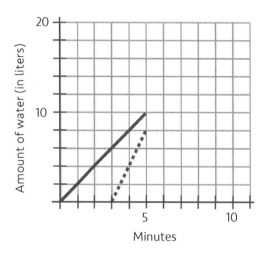

129. Moore's Floors charges $18 per square yard to install new carpeting, with a limited time only $50 fee for removing old carpeting. Doug's Rugs only charges $16 per square yard to install new carpeting, but they have a $225 fee for removing old carpeting.

    a. If you decide to replace your old carpeting, how many square yards would you need to install to make Doug's Rugs the cheaper company to hire for the job?

    b. ★Which company would you choose to replace the carpeting for a rectangular floor that measures 9 yards by 18 yards?

    c. ★What would be the cost for this job?

130. Determine the solution of the system shown. The axis intercepts for both lines are integers.

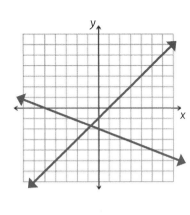

131. You have seen that if $y = 5x + 10$ and $x = 2$, then it follows that $y = 5(2) + 10$ or $y = 20$. Following this principle, if $y = 3M + 1$, and $M = 2x - 3$, then it follows that $y = 3(2x-3)+1$. This can be rewritten as $y =$ _____ , but that isn't too important at this point. The key principle here is that a substitution can be made to replace M with an equivalent expression.

132. ★Suppose $x^2 + y^2 = 25$ and $xy = -12$. What is the value of $(x+y)^2$?

133. Estimate the solution(s) for the system of equations shown in each graph below.

a.

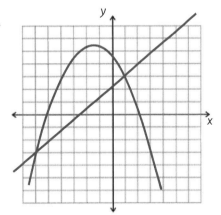

b.

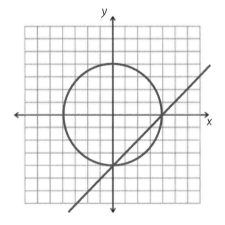

134. ★Determine the solution of the system shown to the right.

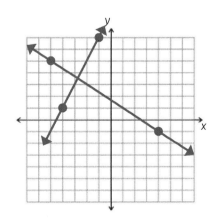

Notes

135. ★Simplify the following fractions.

a. $\dfrac{9x^2 - 4}{18x^3 - 8x}$

b. $\dfrac{3x^2 - 10x + 3}{2x^2 - x - 15}$

136. Solve the equation $x^2 - 4x - 12 = 0$.

137. Solve each equation in the order that it is presented and try to use the order to help you learn an algebraic technique that makes it easier to solve an equation when the variable is in the denominator of a fraction.

a. $\dfrac{x}{2} = 3$

b. $\dfrac{x}{2} = x + 1$

c. $\dfrac{2}{x} = x + 1$

d. $\dfrac{6}{x} + 5 = x$

138. Evaluate the expression $-2x^3 - 3x^2 + x$ if x = -3.

139. Nolan bought a pair of shoes for $93 during a 25% off sale. What was the original shoe price?

140. Simplify each expression as much as you can.

a. $\left(2^2 - 1\right) - \left(5^2 - 3^2\right) \div \left(-2\right)^3$

b. $\left(2x^2 - 3xy - 7y^2\right) - \left(-x^2 + y^2 - 7xy\right)$

c. $\left(3x - 4\right)\left(2x^2 - 5x - 3\right)$

d. -5^0

141. A diver stands at the top of a cliff. He takes a few moments to ensure he is focused and then he falls forward and dives down to a lake below. His path through the air is modeled by the equation

$H = -16t^2 + 64$, where H is his height above the lake, measured in feet, and t is the number of seconds after he falls forward.

    a. At the moment he starts to fall forward, how high above the lake is the diver?

    b. How many seconds has he been falling when he hits the surface of the lake below?

142. Draw a simple sketch of a parabola that has each of the following characteristics.

    a. <u>no x-intercepts; opens downward</u>

                                        b. <u>three x-intercepts; opens upward</u>

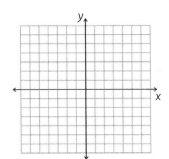 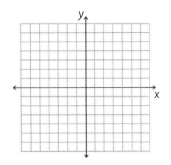

143. Determine the equation of the line that is perpendicular to the line $y = -3x + 1$ and passes through the point $(-3, 4)$. Graph the lines for both equations to confirm that they are perpendicular.

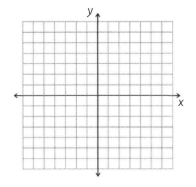

Answer Key

1.	About 7:00am
2.	The intersection point shows two things: 1) how many miles the kids have ridden, and 2) what time it is when the sister catches her brother
3.	(3, 2)
4.	(−4, −1)
5.	a. 12 months b. $2,500 c. $40,000
6.	
7.	$y = mx + b$
8.	a. $y = \dfrac{2}{5}x + 2$ b. $y = -\dfrac{3}{2}x$
9.	a. $y = 3$ b. $x = -4$
10.	a. 1 b. 3 c. 5 d. $\dfrac{1}{2}$
11.	a. 3 b. −16 c. $2\dfrac{1}{8}$ or $\dfrac{17}{8}$ or 2.125
12.	$y = -\dfrac{5}{2}$ or −2.5
13.	$y = -2$
14.	a. $y = -3x + 7$ b. $y = 3x - 7$
15.	$y = \dfrac{4}{5}x - 2$
16.	a. negative b. neither c. positive
17.	Answer revealed later...
18.	Line 1: $y = -x + 1$ Line 2: $y = 2x + 5$
19.	a. 0 b. 7 c. Line 1: $y = 3$; Line 2: $y = 1$ d. Line 1: $x = 2$; Line 2: $x = -3$
20.	1
21.	2
22.	$x = -\dfrac{4}{3}$
23.	a. $y_1 = \dfrac{7}{3}$ b. $y_2 = \dfrac{7}{3}$
24.	$\left(-\dfrac{4}{3}, \dfrac{7}{3}\right)$ or $\left(-1\dfrac{1}{3}, 2\dfrac{1}{3}\right)$
25.	(2, −3)
26.	a. (3, −5) b. $\left(\dfrac{5}{2}, \dfrac{7}{2}\right)$ or (2.5, 3.5)

27.	They intersect at (3, −2). Write equations in Slope-Intercept Form as $y = 3x - 11$ and $y = -4x + 10$.
28.	They intersect at (4, 2). Write equations in Slope-Intercept Form as $y = \dfrac{3}{2}x - 4$ and $y = -\dfrac{3}{4}x + 5$.
29.	$y = \dfrac{1}{2}x + 13$
30.	$\left(\dfrac{8}{3}, \dfrac{40}{3}\right)$
31.	brother: $y = \dfrac{1}{4}x$ sister: $y = \dfrac{2}{3}x - 24$ $x = \dfrac{288}{5}$ minutes (57.6 minutes) At 6:57.6am (approx. 6:58am)
32.	a. $y = 2(5) + 7$ b. $y = 2(10) + 7$ c. $y = 2(2M) + 7$ d. $y = 2(f + 1) + 7$ e. $y = 2(5 - 3y) + 7$
33.	a. $2(y + 2) - 4y = 12$ b. $2(3y - 2) - 4y = 12$ c. $2x - 4(2x - 9) = 12$ d. $2x - 4(-4x - 3) = 12$
34.	a. $2y + 4 - 4y = 12 \rightarrow y = -4$ b. $6y - 4 - 4y = 12 \rightarrow y = 8$ c. $2x - 8x + 36 = 12 \rightarrow x = 4$ d. $2x + 16x + 12 = 12 \rightarrow x = 0$
35.	
36.	$x = 2$
37.	$-6(2) + 2y = -14 \rightarrow y = -1$ $y = -2(2) + 3 \rightarrow y = -1$
38.	(2, −1)
39.	$2(5y + 6) + 3y = -1 \rightarrow y = -1$
40.	intersection point: (1, −1)
41.	$-4x + 3(-6x + 2) = -16 \rightarrow x = 1$ intersection point: (1, −4)
42.	$4\left(\dfrac{1}{2}y - 5\right) - 7y = 10 \rightarrow y = -6$

44

© Alex Joujan, 2013-2018

	intersection point: (−8, −6)
43.	a. (3, 2) b. (10, 0)
44.	a. (−5, −4) b. (24, 11)
45.	(1, 4)
46.	$\left(\dfrac{15}{8}, \dfrac{7}{4}\right)$ or $\left(1\dfrac{7}{8}, 1\dfrac{3}{4}\right)$ or $(1.875, 1.75)$
47.	$\left(-\dfrac{9}{4}, \dfrac{25}{8}\right)$ or $\left(-2\dfrac{1}{4}, 3\dfrac{1}{8}\right)$ or $(-2.25, 3.125)$ The other line's equation is $y = -\dfrac{1}{2}x + 2$.
48.	$\left(\dfrac{8}{3}, \dfrac{7}{3}\right)$; Equations: $y = 2x - 3$, $y = -\dfrac{1}{4}x + 3$
49.	a. A + B b. 7y c. 7x + 2y d. 8x
50.	a. 19 b. 5 c. 9
51.	a. 5x, 3y b. 5x − 2y = −4 c. 3x − 6y = 3
52.	a. 5x + 3y = 4 b. 4x − y = 6 c. −7x + 4y = −3
53.	a. 10y = 20 b. 8x = 80 c. −y = 3
54.	9y
55.	a. 9y = 27 b. 8x + 5y = 7
56.	a. x = −1 b. x = −1 c. If you graph the two equations, the lines will intersect at (−1, 3).
57.	a. 5y = 10 b. 12x = 48 c. −2x + 9y = −3
58.	a. (−1, 2) b. (4, −4) c. The coefficients of the x terms or the y terms must be opposites.
59.	a. 20 b. −3 c. 10
60.	a. 9x − 21y = −36 b. −36x + 8y = 40
61.	Infinite possibilities. Two are shown. $-4x + 3y = 9$ $4x + 12y = -24$ (multiply 2nd eq. by 2) $8x - 6y = -18$ $2x + 6y = -12$ (multiply 1st eq. by −2)
62.	(−3, −1)
63.	(−2, 6)
64.	Substitution
65.	Elimination
66.	Group B. When both equations are in Standard Form, it is easier to group like terms when you add the equations.
67.	a. $\begin{array}{l} -2x - 5y = -2 \\ 2x + 6y = 4 \end{array}$ b. $\begin{array}{l} 2x + 5y = 2 \\ -x - 3y = -2 \end{array}$ c. $\begin{array}{l} x + 3y = 2 \\ 4x + 10y = 4 \end{array}$
68.	a. (−1, 2) b. (4, −4)
69.	(−4, −3)
70.	Yes. Subtraction is adding the opposite so it is a form of addition.
71.	You may make less mistakes when adding.
72.	a. (−5, −4) b. (60, 35)
73.	(18, 8)
74.	a. and b. (−2, −8)
75.	(3.6, 1.4); Equations: $y = -x + 5$, $y = \dfrac{2}{3}x - 1$
76.	(9, 22.5); Equations: $y = \dfrac{5}{2}x$, $y = \dfrac{15}{2}x - 45$
77.	No, if lines are parallel they do not intersect. Also, if two lines are the same line, they intersect everywhere, or at an infinite number of points.
78.	a. The equation has no solution. When you try to solve it, you get an impossible statement, such as 2 = −4, or 0 = 6. b. The equation has infinite solutions. When you try to solve it, you get a statement that is always true, like 10 = 10, or 0 = 0.
79.	The lines do not intersect because they are parallel.
80.	The lines do not intersect because they are parallel. They have the same slopes.
81.	Your work leads to an equation that is false, an equation with no solution. This happens because the lines do not intersect. They have the same slope so they are parallel.
82.	Your work leads to an equation that is always true, an equation with infinite solutions. They intersect everywhere because they are the same line.
83.	a. They intersect everywhere because they are the same line. b. They do not intersect because they have the same slope.
84.	parallel lines
85.	the same line
86.	a. $y = -3x + 6$ b. The solution is 6=6. This equation has infinite solutions.
87.	a. $x = -2y + 10$ b. The solution is 10=10. This equation has infinite solutions.
88.	$w = 8, E = -3$ solve $4w + 2\left(\dfrac{1}{2}w - 7\right) = 26$

45

89.	$m = 8, K = 54$ solve $150 - 12m = 130 - 9.5m$
90.	$f = 21, g = -3$
91.	Equation 1: $13c + 22b = 46290$ Equation 2: $c + b = 3000$ 2190 cars and 810 buses
92.	a. 180°F b. 16 minutes c. 100°F
93.	a. Equation 2: $s + d = 348$ b. Equation 1: $1.99s + 2.99d = 889.52$ 151 single scoop cones
94.	a. $2L + 2W = 12$ b. width: 2cm; length: 4cm define a second equation, $L = W + 2$, and solve the system of equations.
95.	a. $V = 11000 - 800y$ b. $V = 14000 - 1200y$ c. Ford Focus d. 7.5 years
96.	Equation 1: $1x + 3y = 164$ Equation 2: $x + y = 94$ 35 field goals
97.	Equation 1: $D + Q = 788$ Equation 2: $0.1D + 0.25Q = 117.80$ 528 dimes, 260 quarters
98.	You have a collection of nickels and dimes. Instead of counting them by yourself, you bring the coins to a bank. After the coins are counted, you find out that there were 517 coins. The total value of the coins is $41.60. How many coins of each type did you have in the jar?
99.	Equation 1: $P = 80 + 0.20t$ Equation 2: $P = 70 + 0.24t$ a. Cell Allure ($94 vs. $100) b. ($t = 250$) 750 total text messages
100.	Equation 1: $5C + 3.50S = 499$ Equation 2: $C + S = 128$ 34 pounds of king crab 94 pounds of salmon
101.	At a different market, a fisherman sells king crab for $9.20 per pound and salmon for $6 per pound. He sells a total of 85 pounds of crab and salmon and he earns $605. How many pounds of king crab and how many pounds of salmon did he sell?
102.	a. 5 min b. 12 liters c. $y = \dfrac{8}{5}x$ and $y = \dfrac{12}{5}x - 6$
103.	Infinitely many points

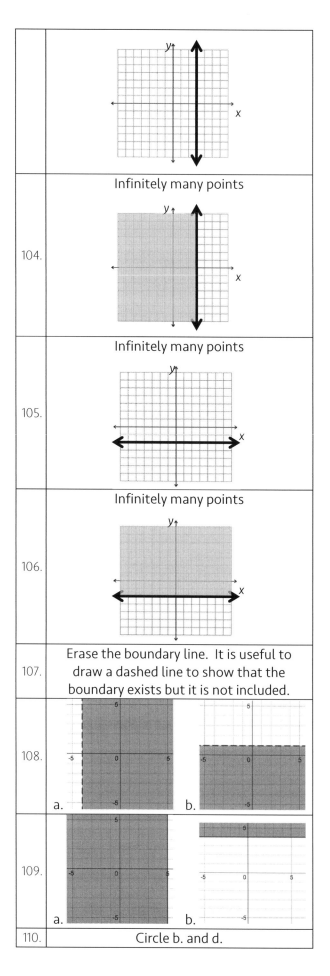

	Infinitely many points
104.	Infinitely many points
105.	Infinitely many points
106.	
107.	Erase the boundary line. It is useful to draw a dashed line to show that the boundary exists but it is not included.
108.	a. b.
109.	a. b.
110.	Circle b. and d.

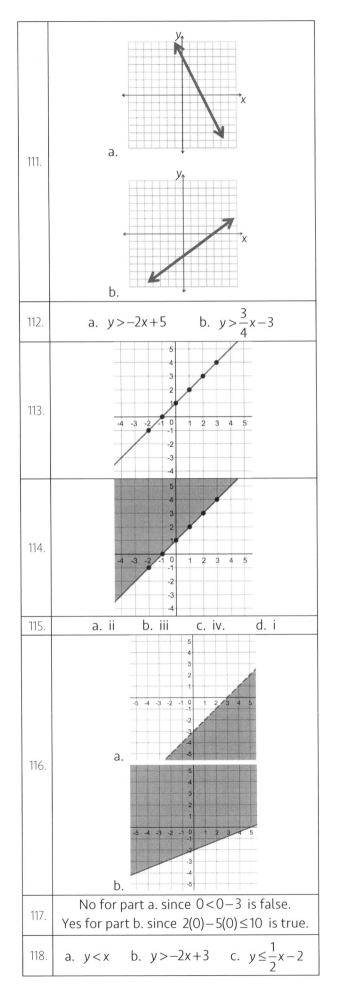

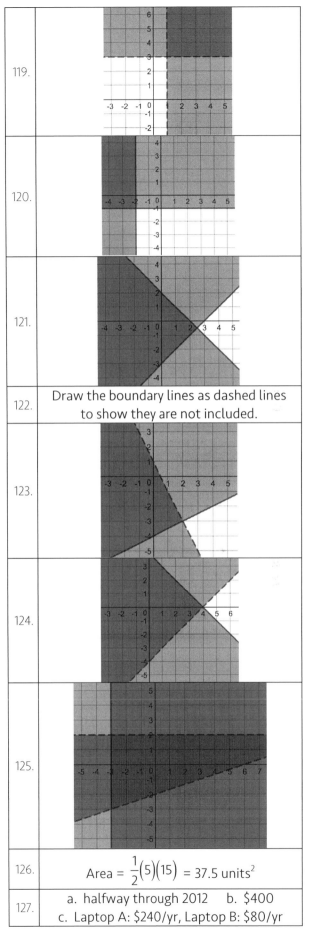

111.

a.

b.

112.   a. $y > -2x + 5$ b. $y > \dfrac{3}{4}x - 3$

113.

114.

115.   a. ii   b. iii   c. iv.   d. i

116.

a.

b.

117. No for part a. since $0 < 0 - 3$ is false.
Yes for part b. since $2(0) - 5(0) \leq 10$ is true.

118.   a. $y < x$ b. $y > -2x + 3$ c. $y \leq \dfrac{1}{2}x - 2$

119.

120.

121.

122. Draw the boundary lines as dashed lines to show they are not included.

123.

124.

125.

126.   Area $= \dfrac{1}{2}(5)(15) = 37.5$ units^2

127.   a. halfway through 2012   b. $400
c. Laptop A: $240/yr, Laptop B: $80/yr

128.	a. b. 4 liters
129.	Moore's Floors: $C = 50 + 18y$ Doug's Rugs: $C = 225 + 16y$ a. more than 87.5 yd^2 b. Doug's Rugs c. cost: \$2,817
130.	$\left(-\dfrac{5}{7}, -1\dfrac{5}{7}\right)$
131.	$y = 6x - 8$
132.	1
133.	a. $(1,3), (-6,-3)$ b. $(4,0), (0,-4)$

134.	$\left(-\dfrac{11}{4}, \dfrac{7}{2}\right)$
135.	a. $\dfrac{1}{2x}$ b. $\dfrac{3x-1}{2x+5}$
136.	$(x-6)(x+2)=0 \rightarrow x=6 \text{ or } -2$
137.	a. 6 b. -2 c. $-2, 1$ d. $6, -1$
138.	$-2(-3)^3 - 3(-3)^2 + -3 \rightarrow -2(-27) - 3(9) - 3$ $54 - 27 - 3 \rightarrow 27 - 3 \rightarrow 24$
139.	\$124
140.	a. 5 b. $3x^2 + 4xy - 8y^2$ c. $6x^3 - 23x^2 + 11x + 12$ d. -1
141.	a. 64 feet b. 2 seconds
142.	a. Answers may vary b. not possible
143.	$y = \dfrac{1}{3}x + 5$

SummitMath

Learn at your **own** pace.

Systems of Equations

Student-centered. Teacher-guided.

Review

1. The average of A and B is 30. The average of A, B, and C is 21. What is the value of C?

2. The population of a small town decreases by 10% in one year to 9,000 people.

    a. How many people were in the town before the decrease?

    b. A common response is to increase 9000 by 10% to find the population last year. Why does this not calculate the original population?

3. In October, a Monarch butterfly begins its southward migration to Mexico. After 8 days of flying, the butterfly is spotted 1200 miles away from its eventual destination. After 12 days of flying, the butterfly is 900 miles away from its destination.

    a. How far will the Monarch have traveled by the time it reaches its destination?

    b. How many total days will it take for the Monarch to arrive at its destination in Mexico?

4. If an ordered pair has an x-value of 0, where will that point be located on the Cartesian plane? If an ordered pair has a y-value of 0, where will it be located on the Cartesian plane?

5. Consider the graph shown to the right.

    a. Identify the x-intercept of the line shown to the right.

    b. Identify the y-intercept of the line shown to the right.

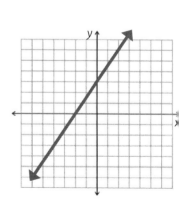

6. Consider the equation $2x + 5y = -10$.

    a. Find the coordinates of the x- and y-intercepts of the equation.

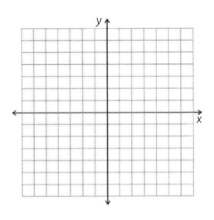

    b. Find the coordinates of one more point on the line and then graph the line.

7. In the graphs below, pick a pair of points and determine the slope of the line. Then pick a different pair of points and find the slope of the line again. Compare your slopes.

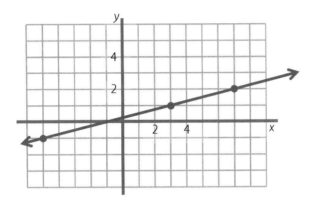

a.

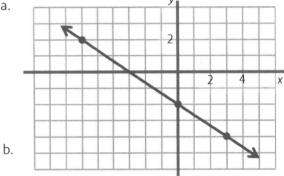

b.

8. Two lines are shown on the Cartesian Plane to the right.

    a. What is the slope of the dashed line?

    b. What is the slope of the solid line?

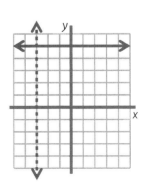

9. What is the equation of the line that passes through $(-1, -4)$ and $(-6, 11)$?

10. Simplify each expression as much as you can, using only positive exponents in your answer.

   a. $2x \cdot 3x^2$

   b. 3^{-2}

   c. $\dfrac{2x^{-4}}{3y^{-1}}$

   d. $\left(x^{-2}\right)^2$

11. Simplify each expression as much as you can.

   a. $2x + 3x$

   b. $2x + 3y$

   c. $\left(x+3\right)^2$

   d. $\left(2x-1\right)\left(2x+1\right)$

12. Factor each of the following expressions as much as you can.

   a. $x^2 - 8x + 16$

   b. $2x^2 - 6x$

   c. $2x^2 - 7x - 9$

   d. $18 - 2x^2$

13. The following equations are written in Standard Form, Ax + By = C. Rearrange the equations to write them in Slope-Intercept Form, y = mx + b.

   a. $x + y = 3$

   b. $3x - 2y = 6$

   c. $-5x - 10y = 7$

14. The following inequalities are written in Standard Form. Rearrange them to write them in Slope-Intercept Form.

   a. $x + y < 3$

   b. $3x - 2y \geq 6$

   c. $-5x - 10y < 7$

15. Did you forget to switch the direction of the inequality in the previous scenario? Whenever you rearrange an inequality, when do you need to reverse the direction of the inequality symbol?

Introduction to intersecting lines

16. Looking at the graph shown, where do the two lines intersect?

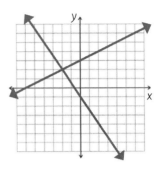

17. A beetle challenges a caterpillar to a race, but she wants to be fair so she gives the caterpillar a head start.

    a. If they both move at constant speeds for the entire race, who wins the race?

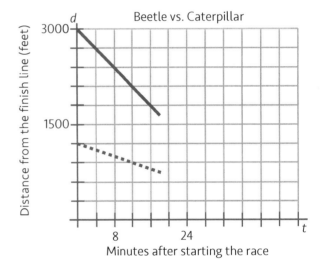

    b. The beetle gave the caterpillar a head start of how many feet?

    c. How fast do they each move, measured in feet per minute?

18. In the previous scenario, after how many minutes will the caterpillar finish the race?

19. Use the graph for the previous scenario to write an equation that models the beetle's race. Make the equation show the relationship between the beetle's distance from the finish line, d (measured in feet), and the total number of minutes the beetle has been moving, t.

20. Prove that the following lines intersect at (3, 2) by graphing the two lines.

Line 1: $y = -x + 5$

Line 2: $y = 2x - 4$

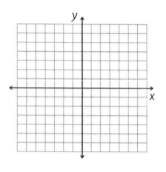

21. Determine the equation of each line shown. Although there are various forms that you can use when you write the equation of a line, like Standard Form and Point-Slope Form, write your equation in Slope-Intercept Form for now.

a.

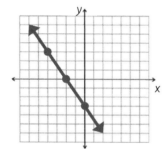

b.

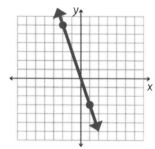

c.

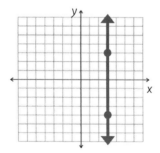

d.

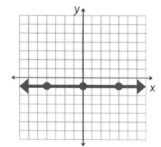

22. Rearrange your equations in the previous scenario to write them in Standard Form. As a reminder, the Standard Form of a linear equation is Ax + By = C.

54

23. Consider the equation $y = -x + 10$.

    a. If the value of x is 0, then the value of y is $-(0) + 10$, or ___.

    b. If the value of x is -1, then y is ___.

    c. For what x-value does $y = 0$?

24. Now consider the equation $y = -\dfrac{3}{2}x - 2$.

    a. If the value of x is $x = -\dfrac{4}{5}$, then y is _____.   b. For what x-value does $y = 4$?

25. For the equation $y = \dfrac{1}{4}x + 1$, what is the value of y if $x = -\dfrac{8}{9}$?

26. ★For the equation $y = -\dfrac{5}{6}x + 4$, what is the value of y if $x = -1\dfrac{3}{5}$?

27. Consider the equation $2x - 3y = 7$.

    a. Replace "x" with the expression "$3y - 7$" and solve the resulting equation.

    b. Start over. Now replace "y" with the expression "$\frac{4}{3}x - 1$" and solve the resulting equation.

28. Rearrange the equation $5x - 4y = 12$ to write it in Slope-Intercept Form.

29. One line is formed by the equation $y = 2x - 8$. A second line is formed by the equation $y = -3x + 12$. Without graphing them, where do these two lines intersect?

30. Find the intersection point of the two lines below.

$$y = \frac{3}{4}x + 1$$
$$y = -x - 13$$

31. Determine the equations of Line 1 and Line 2.

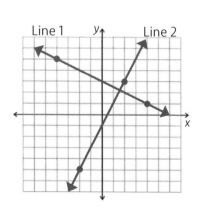

32. Use either the equations or the graphs of Lines 1 and 2 in the previous scenario to answer the following questions.

    a. What are the *y*-values of Lines 1 and 2 when *x* = −2?

    b. What are the *x*-values of Lines 1 and 2 when *y* = 0?

33. In the previous scenario, where do Lines 1 and 2 intersect?

34. Determine the intersection point of the graphs of $y=\frac{1}{4}x-7$ and $y=-x+3$.

35. Where do the graphs of $4x-5y=10$ and $30-10y=2x$ intersect?

36. Where do the two lines intersect? They are shown in the graph and their equations are shown below.

$$y = -3x + 3$$
$$y = 2x - 3$$

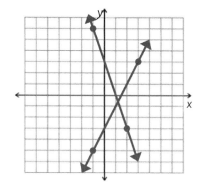

37. Consider the line shown in the graph. Write the equation of the line in Slope-Intercept Form.

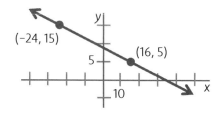

(−24, 15)

(16, 5)

5

10

38. How can you find the exact coordinates of a line's x-intercept if you know the equation of the line?

39. What is the location of the x-intercept of the line $y = -\dfrac{1}{4}x + 9$?

40. Consider the graph shown to the right.

   a. Determine the equations of the two lines.

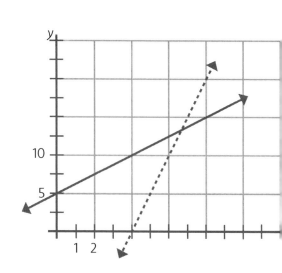

   b. Determine the intersection point of the two lines.

41. Consider the equation $y=6x-11$.

    a. What is the value of y if x is replaced with 3?

    d. Rewrite the equation if x is replaced with "y + 1".

42. In the previous scenario, when x is replaced with another expression, the original equation now contains only 1 variable. Solve for y in each equation in the previous scenario.

43. Now consider the equation $-5x+3y=30$.

    a. Rewrite the equation if x is replaced with "y – 7".

    b. Rewrite the equation if $y = -2x - 1$".

44. In the equation $-5x+3y=30$, there are two variables, x and y. In the previous scenario, when one of the variables is replaced with another expression, the resulting equation contains only one variable. Solve each of these resulting equations.

45. Consider Line 1, $y=\dfrac{1}{3}x+1$, and Line 2, $4x-3y=15$.

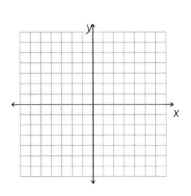

    a. Graph both of the lines in the Cartesian plane.

    b. In the equation $4x-3y=15$, replace the y with $\dfrac{1}{3}x+1$. An equation with two variables now contains only one variable. Solve this equation.

46. Your calculations in the previous scenario should reveal that the lines intersect when $x = 6$.

    a. If you did not get this result, go back through your work and try to find your error. You may have forgotten to use the Distributive Property after replacing y with $\frac{1}{3}x+1$.

    b. Line 1 and Line 2 intersect at a single point with an x-value of 6. They should have the same y-value when you replace x with 6 in each equation. Verify this by replacing x with 6 in each equation and solving the resulting equation.

The method you just used is known as the Substitution Method because you allow an equivalent expression $\left(\frac{1}{3}x+1\right)$ to serve as a substitute for another variable: y.

47. Consider another pair of equations: $y=\frac{3}{4}x-4$ and $x+4y=8$. Rewrite the equation $x+4y=8$ to isolate x.

48. In the equation $y=\frac{3}{4}x-4$, replace the x-value with the equivalent expression that you found in the previous scenario. Now that the equation only contains the variable y, solve for y.

49. Determine the intersection point of the lines $y=\frac{3}{4}x-4$ and $x+4y=8$.

Your work should reveal that the Substitution Method allows you to determine where two lines intersect. You can make a substitution for either variable, whichever is easier to isolate.

50. Determine the intersection point of each pair of lines using the Substitution Method.

    a.
$$5x+2y=19$$
$$y=3x-7$$

    b.
$$2x+5y=5$$
$$x=7y-7$$

A pair of lines is called a <u>system of equations</u>. The intersection point of a system of equations is often called the <u>solution</u> of that system.

51. Find the solution of each system of equations below. Use the Substitution Method.

a.
$$y=-\frac{3}{4}x+2$$
$$-2x+4y=28$$

b.
$$3x-5y=3$$
$$x=-\frac{1}{3}y+4$$

52. Solve the system of equations below.

$$-4x-8y=8$$
$$3x-2y=10$$

53. Glenna found the intersection of the lines below. Her solution is (6, 3).

$$y=-x+9$$
$$-3x+7y=5$$

a. Without graphing the lines, how can she prove that her solution is correct?

b. Do your own calculations to prove that Glenna is correct.

54. Use the Substitution Method to solve each system shown.

$$-3x - y = 19$$
$$5x - \frac{1}{2}y = 3$$

55. Use the Substitution Method to solve each system shown.

$$9x - 4y = 11$$
$$-4x + 2y = 6$$

56. Where do the two lines intersect?

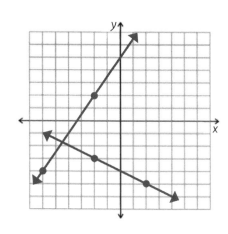

57. A beetle challenges a caterpillar to a race, but she wants to be fair so she gives the caterpillar a head start. She eventually catches the caterpillar because she runs much faster.

How far was the beetle from the finish line at the exact moment that she caught up to the caterpillar?

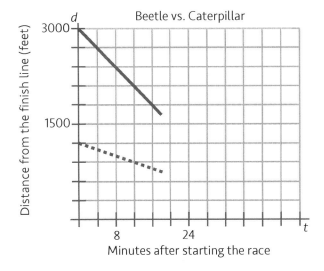

58. How does finding the exact moment when the beetle catches the caterpillar relate to the mathematical topic of systems of equations?

63

The Elimination Method

Now that you have gained familiarity with the Substitution Method, you will learn about one more method for finding the intersection point of two lines. This next method uses basic arithmetic (addition, subtraction, etc...) and a helpful amount of logical reasoning.

59. Consider the following scenarios. In each scenario, you are given two complete equations. Use those equations to determine the missing information in the incomplete third equation.

    a. If $A = 6x + 5y$ and $B = x - 4y$, then $A + B =$ _____ .

    b. If $3x - y = 50$ and $2x + 9y = 50$, then _____ $= 100$.

60. Fill in the missing information in the third equation.

    a. If $-7x + 8y = 22$ and $9x + 2y = 8$, then $2x + 10y =$ _____ .

    b. If $-5x + 7y = 9$ and $4x - 2y = 1$, then $-x + 5y =$ _____ .

    c. If $2x - 4y = 1$ and $6x - 3y = 10$, then $10x - 11y =$ _____ .

61. Fill in the missing equation to make each addition scenario true.

    a. $\begin{array}{r} 2x+5y=3 \\ +\underline{\hspace{3cm}} \\ 7x+8y=7 \end{array}$
    b. $\begin{array}{r} 3x+2y=7 \\ +\underline{\hspace{3cm}} \\ 8x+0y=3 \end{array}$
    c. $\begin{array}{r} -2x+6y=10 \\ +\underline{\hspace{3cm}} \\ x+0y=13 \end{array}$

62. Fill in the missing equation to make each addition scenario true.

    a. $\begin{array}{r} 7x+8y=7 \\ -\underline{\hspace{3cm}} \\ 2x+5y=3 \end{array}$
    b. $\begin{array}{r} 4x+y=9 \\ -\underline{\hspace{3cm}} \\ 0x+2y=3 \end{array}$
    c. $\begin{array}{r} -6x+4y=5 \\ -\underline{\hspace{3cm}} \\ x+0y=8 \end{array}$

63. Since subtraction can get challenging at times, we will focus only on adding equations. Combine each pair of equations by <u>adding downward</u>. This will create a new equation.

    a. $\begin{array}{l} -x+4y=10 \\ x+5y=8 \end{array}$
    b. $\begin{array}{l} 9x-8y=5 \\ 2x+8y=50 \end{array}$
    c. $\begin{array}{l} 3x-4y=-4 \\ -x+4y=16 \end{array}$

64. Consider two equations: $7x + y = 15$ and $3x - y = 5$.

If $7x + y = 15$ and $3x - y = 5$, then _____ = 20

65. Look at the previous scenario again. Line up the equations to write one above the other.

$7x + y = 15$
$3x - y = 5$

Now complete the following operations. In part a., combine the two equations by adding downward. In part b. combine the two equations by subtracting downward.

a. ADD
$7x + y = 15$
$3x - y = 5$

b. SUBTRACT (be careful!)
$7x + y = 15$
$3x - y = 5$

66. When you subtract the two equations in the previous scenario, the resulting equation is still a two-variable equation $(4x + 2y = 10)$, so it remains unsolvable. However, when you add the two equations, the resulting equation is $10x = 20$. Mental math quickly reveals that $x = 2$.

a. Replace x with 2 in the equation $7x + y = 15$ and solve for y.

b. Replace x with 2 in the equation $3x - y = 5$ and solve for y.

c. Explain the significance of what you find.

67. Combine each pair of equations by adding downward. This will create a new equation.

a.
$-9x + 10y = 18$
$9x + 5y = 12$

b.
$-3x + 20y = 70$
$11x - 20y = -6$

c.
$3x + 4y = 14$
$-5x + 2y = 20$

68. In the previous scenario, when you have two equations with two variables and you combine the equations by adding downward, one of the variables might be eliminated, although in part c., this does not occur. This elimination is helpful because it converts a pair of 2-variable equations into a single 1-variable equation. Why is neither variable eliminated by subtraction in part c.?

In part c., when you add the two equations, you need to change a coefficient in one of the equations to eliminate a variable. It would be easy if you could just change a number that you see and replace it with one that you want. In a sense, you can do that, as long as you are careful about how you do it. You can change an equation by multiplying both sides by the same number.

69. Fill in the blanks in each statement below.

   a. $x + 4y = 9$ is the same equation as $3x + 12y =$ _____ .

   b. $2x - 4y = 11$ is the same equation as _____ $x + 32y =$ _____ .

   c. $-5x + 9y = -5$ is the same equation as _____ $x +$ _____ $y = 25$.

70. Change the appearance of one or both of the equations shown below to make addition eliminate one of the variables. Change the equation(s), but do not perform the addition.

$$3x + 4y = 14$$
$$-5x + 2y = 20$$

71. Determine the intersection point of the graphs of $3x + 4y = 14$ and $-5x + 2y = 20$.

72. The Elimination Method is a strategy that involves adding two equations to eliminate one of the variables. Use the Elimination Method to determine the intersection of the pair of lines below.

$$3x + 6y = 30$$
$$2x - 6y = 20$$

73. Use the Elimination Method to find the intersection point of each pair of lines below.

a.
$$-2x+7y=6$$
$$2x-3y=2$$

b.
$$-x-7y=18$$
$$x-2y=9$$

74. The Elimination Method is easier to use if you rewrite the equations in Standard Form ($Ax + By = C$). This makes it easier to group like terms when you add the equations. Rewrite each pair of equations to put them both in Standard Form, but **do not** do any further calculations.

a.
$$6x-2y=13$$
$$11=5y-3x$$

b.
$$x-9y=32$$
$$8+3y=-3x$$

75. Rewrite the equations below to put them both in Standard Form, but **do not** do any further calculations. You only need to rewrite the equation that is currently in Slope-Intercept Form.

$$y=\frac{1}{2}x-\frac{5}{2}$$
$$7x-9y=15$$

76. The Elimination Method has been described as a strategy that involves <u>adding</u> two equations. Do you think it would work to subtract two equations? Explain your reasoning.

77. Determine the intersection of each pair of lines by <u>subtracting</u> the equations to eliminate one of the variables. The first one is started for you to show you a way to organize your work.

a.
$$x+3y=12$$
$$-\ (x+y=8)$$

b.
$$3x+5y=14$$
$$x+5y=8$$

c.
$$-4x+y=8$$
$$-4x-2y=-4$$

78. It was mentioned in an earlier scenario that finding the intersection point of two lines is also called "solving a systems of equation." Do not solve the system of equations below. Instead, explain how you would change the equations in order to make it easier to use the Elimination Method.

$$y=-\frac{3}{4}x+2$$
$$-2x+4y=28$$

79. Use the Elimination Method to solve each system of equations.

a.
$$2x+5y=5$$
$$x=7y-7$$

b.
$$-4x-8y=8$$
$$3x-2y=10$$

80. ★Use substitution to find the intersection point of the lines $3x-9y=-18$ and $5y-2x=4$.

When two lines do not intersect at a single point

81. This may seem like review, but solve each equation below.

    a. $x+3-2x=-(x-3)$ b. $2x=\frac{1}{3}(6x-12)+9$

82. Two lines are shown in the graph. Where do they intersect?

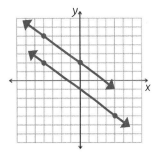

83. Graph the two lines shown below. Using the graph, where do the lines intersect?

    $y=-\frac{1}{5}x+4$ and $y=-\frac{1}{5}x-3$

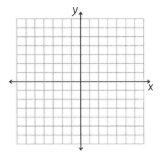

84. Graph the two lines shown below. Using the graph, where do the lines intersect?

    $y=2x-5$ and $2x-y=5$

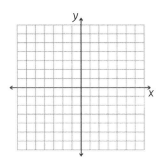

85. Without graphing, determine the intersection point of each pair of lines. Use any method. Graph the two equations to confirm that your intersection point is accurate.

a.
$$-x+2y=14$$
$$3x-6y=-36$$

b.
$$-3x-y=2$$
$$6x=-4-2y$$

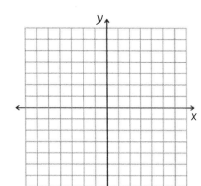
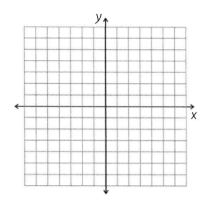

86. Without graphing (use either Substitution or Elimination), determine the intersection point of the graphs of $12+6y=2x$ and $3y=x+6$.

87. Once again, without graphing (use either Substitution or Elimination), determine the intersection point of the graphs of $60-8x=20y$ and $2x+5y=15$.

88. When you substitute an equation into itself, what is the result and why does this happen?

Scenarios that involve systems of equations

You have solved systems equations containing only x's and y's. If these variables are changed to other letters, it may seem confusing at first, but it does not change anything about what you have learned.

89. Use the **substitution** method to find the values of h and R that make both equations true.

$$R = 27 - 5.4h$$
$$R = -43 + 1.6h$$

90. Use the **elimination** method to find the values of d and h that make both equations true.

$$2.1d - 1.4h = 63$$
$$d + h = 80$$

91. At the end of a busy day at the county fair, an accountant records the earnings. The fair sells tickets for children at $7.50 per ticket and tickets for adults at $10.50 per ticket. On this particular day, 680 people came to the fair and the earnings for the day totaled $6,195.00. How many tickets for children were purchased?

92. A collection of pennies and quarters is worth $10.26. There are a total of 402 coins in the collection. How many coins of each type are there?

93. At a farmer's market one week, you pay $9.75 for 5 pounds of potatoes and 2 pounds of carrots. A couple weeks later, you buy 4 pounds of potatoes and 5 pounds of carrots and pay $13.75.

    a. What is the price per pound for carrots?

    b. How much would you pay for 3 pounds of potatoes and 3 pounds of carrots?

94. After a recent earthquake destroyed the homes of thousands of families, a relief agency sent boxes filled with food and crates filled with clothing to help provide for their necessities. Each box was filled with 60 pounds of food and each crate was filled with 24 pounds of clothing.

    a. The agency sent a total of 3,086 boxes and crates and the total weight of these supplies was 147,000 pounds. How many boxes of food did they send?

    b. How many pounds of clothing did they send?

95. Another relief agency sent boxes filled with food and crates filled with clothing to the families affected by the earthquake in the previous scenario. Two equations are shown below.

$$B + C = 856$$
$$35B + 17C = 16,514$$

    a. What was the total weight of the supplies that this relief agency sent to the families?

    b. How many pounds of food did each of their boxes contain?

96. Melissa and Collin work for a business that makes unpainted, wooden pencils. Melissa cuts each pencil to a specific length and then she hands it to Collin, who attaches an eraser onto the end. Melissa gets to work one day and starts cutting. She cut the pencils at a rate of 10 pencils per minute. Collin gets to work 15 minutes late and starts putting on the erasers. Collin puts on erasers at a rate of 12 erasers per minute. Since Collin arrives late, he has a large pile of pencils waiting for him when he starts working. How many minutes will Collin have to work before he catches up to Melissa and he no longer has unfinished pencils sitting in a pile in front of him?

97. The length of a rectangle is 3 inches longer than twice the length of the width. The perimeter of the rectangle is 36 inches. What are the dimensions of the rectangle?

98. Two neighbors drain their pools at the end of the summer. Elaine's pool contains 12,500 gallons of water and her pump empties her pool at a rate of 30 gallons per minute. Doris's pool is filled with 14,000 gallons of water and her pump rate is 45 gallons per minute. Doris and Elaine start draining their pools at the same time and then they go for a walk together.

   a. After the pumps have been running for 30 minutes, which pool contains more water? How many more gallons does it contain?

   b. When Doris and Elaine get back from their walk, their pools contain the same amount of water. How long was their walk?

99. A blue-painted tank contains 1200 gallons of water. A red-painted tank contains 160 gallons of water. When a valve is opened, water flows from the blue tank into the red tank at a rate of 20 gallons per minute. If the valve is opened at 8:00am, at what time will the two tanks contain the same amount of water?

100. Two planes fly toward each other going in opposite directions. One plane is flying away from Seattle and the other plane is flying toward Seattle. The motion of the one plane is modeled by the equation $D = 600 + 500h$, where D is the distance, in miles, between the plane and Seattle and h is the number of hours after 3pm. The motion of the other plane, using the same variables, is modeled by the equation $D = 1,920 - 400h$.

    a. At what time will the planes pass each other in the sky?

    b. At what rate is each airplane flying, in miles per hour?

    c. Is the faster plane or the slower plane flying toward Seattle? How do you know?

Linear Inequalities and Systems of Linear Inequalities

101. Graph each inequality.

a. $y > 3$

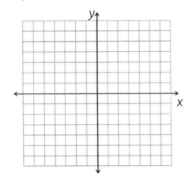

b. $x \le -4$

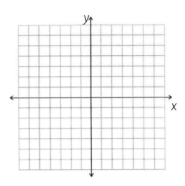

102. Circle each inequality that would have a shaded region that includes the boundary line.

a. $x + y \le 7$ b. $y > 5x + 2$ c. $-x + 4y \le 8$ d. $y > -2$

103. Match each inequality with its graph.

a. $y \le -\dfrac{2}{3}x + 2$ b. $y \ge -x + 3$ c. $y < -x - 3$ d. $y \ge -\dfrac{2}{3}x + 2$

i.

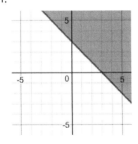

ii.

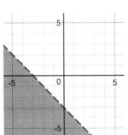

iii.

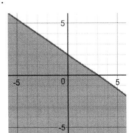

iv.

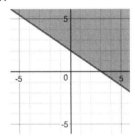

104. Isolate the variable y in the inequality below.

a. $3x + 5y < -30$ b. $-3y + 9x \ge 24$

105. Graph each inequality.

a. $y \geq -x + 2$

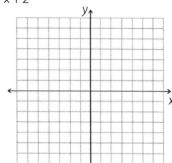

b. $x - 4y > 12$

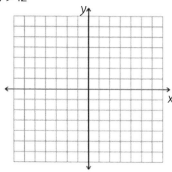

106. Write the inequality that has the solution set shown in each graph below.

a.

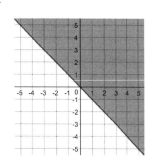

b.

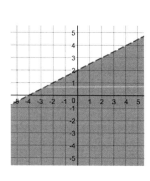

c.

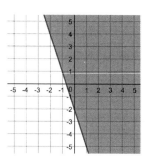

107. The lines in the graph shown divide the plane into 4 regions. Shade in the region that satisfies the 2 inequalities below.

$$y < \frac{1}{2}x - 2$$
$$y \leq -2x + 3$$

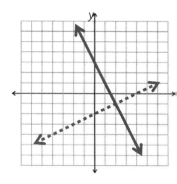

108. Display the solution of the system of inequalities. This is also known as graphing the system.

$$y \geq 3$$
$$x < -4$$

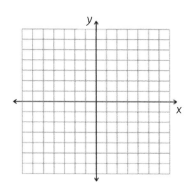

109. Graph the system of inequalities.

$$y \geq -\frac{1}{3}x + 2$$
$$y < 3x - 4$$

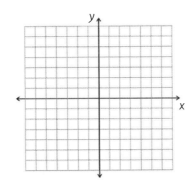

110. Graph the system of inequalities.

$$y + x \geq -3$$
$$y - x > -1$$

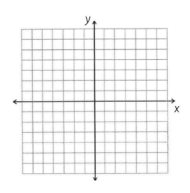

111. Graph the system of inequalities.

$$x < 2$$
$$y > -1$$
$$2y - x < 8$$

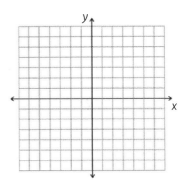

112. Calculate the area of the triangular shaded region in the previous scenario.

113. Write the next 9 numbers in the sequence shown below.

1, 4, 9, 16, 25, 36, . . .

114. Write the next 4 numbers in the sequence shown below.

1, 8, 27, 64, . . .

115. Try to write the next 4 numbers in the sequence shown below.

$4, \ -2, \ 1, \ -\dfrac{1}{2}, \ . . .$

116. Solve the equation. $5(3x+2)=2-x$

117. Simplify each expression as much as you can, using only positive exponents in your answer.

a. $\dfrac{16x^2 y^{-2}}{10xy^3}$
b. $\left(2^{-2}\right)^3$
c. $7p^{-1}$
d. $\left(3x^{-2}\right)^{-2}$

118. Calculate the area of the triangle formed by the three lines.

  Line 1: $y = x + 3$

  Line 2: $2x + y = 6$

  Line 3: $y + 4 = 0$

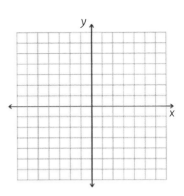

119. Draw a simple sketch of a parabola that has each of the following characteristics.

  a. two x-intercepts; opens upward

  b. one x-intercept; opens downward

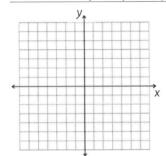
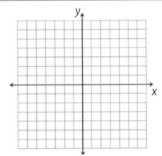

120. What is the equation of the line that passes through the origin and never crosses the line $3x - 5y = 15$? Graph the lines for both equations to confirm your result.

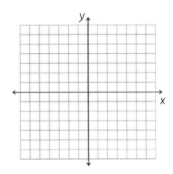

121. On January 1, 2010, a house was valued at $200,000. On January 1, 2011, the value of the house had decreased by 10%. On January 1, 2012, the value of the house had increased by 10%. On January 1, 2012, was the value of the house greater than, less than, or equal to $200,000? Try to support your answer with an explanation as well as calculations.

122. Multiply or divide the fractions and simplify your result as much as possible.

a. $\dfrac{4}{9y^2} \cdot \dfrac{12y}{8} \cdot 3y$

b. $\dfrac{6x}{11} \div \dfrac{48x^2}{33}$

123. Add or subtract the fractions and simplify your result as much as possible.

a. $\dfrac{2}{7} + \dfrac{2}{3}$

b. $\dfrac{2x}{4} - \dfrac{7x}{6}$

124. Combine the fractions. Simplify the result as much as possible.

a. $\dfrac{3x^2 - 7}{x-2} + \dfrac{3-2x^2}{x-2}$

b. $\dfrac{1+4x}{x+3} - \dfrac{6x+7}{x+3}$

125. Simplify each expression as much as you can.

a. $\sqrt{25}$

b. $\sqrt{81}$

c. $\sqrt{\dfrac{1}{4}}$

★d. $\sqrt{\dfrac{36}{49}}$

1.	A+B = 60 and A+B+C = 63, so C = 3
2.	a. equation: 0.9P=9,000 so P=10,000 b. The original population decreases by 10%, which is not the same result as increasing the new population by 10%.
3.	a. 1800 miles b. 24 days
4.	a. on the y-axis b. on the x-axis
5.	a. x-int: (–2, 0) b. y-int: (0, 3)
6.	a. To find the x-int, replace y with 0 in the equation and solve for x. To find the y-int, replace x with 0 in the equation and solve for y. x-int: (–5, 0) y-int: (0, –2) b. Graph:
7.	a. $\dfrac{1}{4}$ b. $-\dfrac{2}{3}$
8.	a. undefined b. 0
9.	$y=-3x-7$
10.	a. $6x^3$ b. $\dfrac{1}{9}$ c. $\dfrac{2y}{3x^4}$ d. $\dfrac{1}{x^4}$
11.	a. $5x$ b. $2x+3y$ c. x^2+6x+9 d. $4x^2-1$
12.	a. $(x-4)^2$ b. $2x(x-3)$ c. $(2x-9)(x+1)$ d. $2(3+x)(3-x)$
13.	a. $y = -x + 3$ b. $y=\dfrac{3}{2}x-3$ c. $y=-\dfrac{1}{2}x-\dfrac{7}{10}$
14.	a. $y < -x + 3$ b. $y\le\dfrac{3}{2}x-3$ c. $y>-\dfrac{1}{2}x-\dfrac{7}{10}$
15.	When you multiply by a negative number or divide by a negative number on both sides of the inequality, the direction of the inequality symbol must be switched.
16.	(–2, 2)

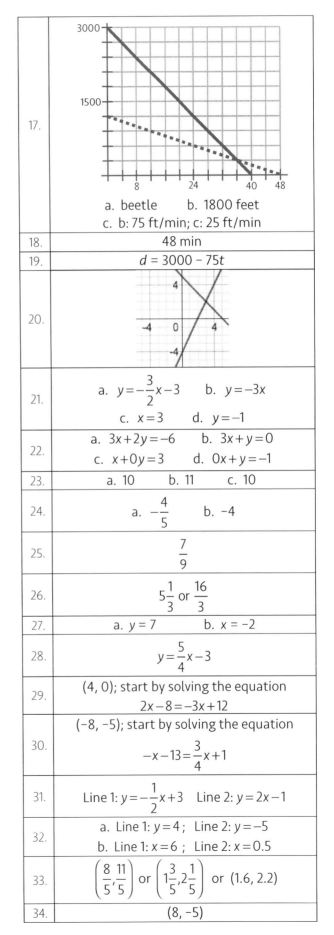

17.	a. beetle b. 1800 feet c. b: 75 ft/min; c: 25 ft/min
18.	48 min
19.	$d = 3000 - 75t$
20.	
21.	a. $y=-\dfrac{3}{2}x-3$ b. $y=-3x$ c. $x=3$ d. $y=-1$
22.	a. $3x+2y=-6$ b. $3x+y=0$ c. $x+0y=3$ d. $0x+y=-1$
23.	a. 10 b. 11 c. 10
24.	a. $-\dfrac{4}{5}$ b. –4
25.	$\dfrac{7}{9}$
26.	$5\dfrac{1}{3}$ or $\dfrac{16}{3}$
27.	a. $y = 7$ b. $x = -2$
28.	$y=\dfrac{5}{4}x-3$
29.	(4, 0); start by solving the equation $2x-8=-3x+12$
30.	(–8, –5); start by solving the equation $-x-13=\dfrac{3}{4}x+1$
31.	Line 1: $y=-\dfrac{1}{2}x+3$ Line 2: $y=2x-1$
32.	a. Line 1: $y=4$; Line 2: $y=-5$ b. Line 1: $x=6$; Line 2: $x=0.5$
33.	$\left(\dfrac{8}{5},\dfrac{11}{5}\right)$ or $\left(1\dfrac{3}{5},2\dfrac{1}{5}\right)$ or (1.6, 2.2)
34.	(8, –5)

35.	(5, 2)
36.	$\left(\dfrac{6}{5}, -\dfrac{3}{5}\right)$ Equation 1: $y = -3x + 3$ Equation 2: $y = 2x - 3$
37.	$y = -\dfrac{1}{4}x + 9$
38.	In the equation, replace y with 0 and solve for x.
39.	(36, 0)
40.	a. solid: $y = \dfrac{5}{4}x + 5$ dashed: $y = 5x - 20$ b. $\left(\dfrac{20}{3}, \dfrac{40}{3}\right)$ or $\left(6\dfrac{2}{3}, 13\dfrac{1}{3}\right)$
41.	a. $y = 6(3) - 11$ b. $y = 6(y+1) - 11$
42.	a. $y = 7$ b. $y = 6y + 6 - 11 \rightarrow -5y = -5 \rightarrow y = 1$
43.	a. $-5(y-7) + 3y = 30$ b. $-5x + 3(-2x-1) = 30$
44.	a. $-5y + 35 + 3y = 30 \rightarrow -2y = -5 \rightarrow y = 2.5$ b. $-5x - 6x - 3 = 30 \rightarrow -11x = 33 \rightarrow x = -3$
45.	 a. b. $x = 6$
46.	a. - b. $y = 3$
47.	$x = 8 - 4y$
48.	$y = \dfrac{3}{4}(8 - 4y) - 4 \ \rightarrow\ y = \dfrac{1}{2}$
49.	$\left(6, \dfrac{1}{2}\right)$
50.	a. (3, 2) b. (0, 1)
51.	a. (-4, 5) b. (3.5, 1.5)
52.	(2, -2)
53.	a. Plug the point into BOTH of the equations to show that each equation is TRUE when the point is substituted into the equation. b. The solution is not correct. The point (6,3) is on the line $y = -x + 9$, but it is NOT on the line $-3x + 7y = 5$. The <u>exact</u> solution is (5.8, 3.2).
54.	(-1, -16)

55.	(23, 49)
56.	$\left(-\dfrac{9}{2}, -\dfrac{7}{4}\right)$ Equation 1: $y = -\dfrac{1}{2}x - 4$ Equation 2: $y = \dfrac{3}{2}x + 5$
57.	Exactly 300 feet (after 36 minutes) Caterpillar Equation: $d = -25t + 1200$ Beetle Equation: $d = -75t + 3000$
58.	Use the equations of the lines to find the exact point where the two lines cross. The x-value of that intersection point is the time and the y-value is the distance from the finish line.
59.	a. $7x + y$ b. $5x + 8y$
60.	a. 30 b. 10 c. 12
61.	a. $5x + 3y = 4$ b. $5x - 2y = -4$ c. $3x - 6y = 3$
62.	a. $5x + 3y = 4$ b. $4x - y = 6$ c. $-7x + 4y = -3$
63.	a. $9y = 18$ b. $11x = 55$ c. $2x = 12$
64.	$10x$
65.	a. $10x = 20$ b. $4x + 2y = 10$
66.	a. $y = 1$ b. $y = 1$ c. If you graph the two equations, the lines will intersect at (2, 1).
67.	a. $15y = 30$ b. $8x = 64$ b. $-2x + 6y = 34$
68.	Neither the coefficients of the x terms nor the y terms are opposites.
69.	a. 27 b. -16, -88 c. 25, -45
70.	Option 1: multiply both sides of the bottom equation by -2 $3x + 4y = 14$ $10x - 4y = -40$ Option 2: multiply the top equation by 5 and the bottom equation by 3 $15x + 20y = 70$ $-15x + 6y = 60$ Other options are also possible.
71.	(-2, 5)
72.	(10, 0)
73.	a. (4, 2) b. (3, -3)
74.	a. $\begin{array}{l} 6x - 2y = 13 \\ -3x + 5y = 11 \end{array}$ b. $\begin{array}{l} x - 9y = 32 \\ 3x + 3y = -8 \end{array}$
75.	$-\dfrac{1}{2}x + y = -\dfrac{5}{2} \rightarrow -2\cdot\left(-\dfrac{1}{2}x + y\right) = \left(-\dfrac{5}{2}\right)\cdot -2$ $\rightarrow x - 2y = 5$
76.	Yes, it would. Subtraction involves adding

	the opposite value. If you want to avoid subtraction, you have that choice, but it is a valid option.
77.	a. (6, 2) b. (3, 1) c. (–1, 4)
78.	Rewrite the equation $y=-\dfrac{3}{4}x+2$ as shown below to put it in Standard Form. $$\dfrac{3}{4}x+y=2 \rightarrow 4\cdot\left(\dfrac{3}{4}x+y\right)=2\cdot4 \rightarrow 3x+4y=8$$
79.	a. (0, 1) b. (2, –2)
80.	(18, 8)
81.	a. The equation has infinite solutions. When you solve it, you get a statement that is always true, like 3 = 3, or 0 = 0. b. The equation has no solution. When you solve it, you get an impossible statement, such as 0 = 5.
82.	They do not intersect. They are parallel. Equation 1: $y=-\dfrac{3}{4}x+2$ Equation 2: $y=-\dfrac{3}{4}x-1$
83.	They do not intersect because the lines are parallel.
84.	Both equations represent the same line. Since the two lines are the same line, they intersect infinitely many times.
85.	a. No solution b. Infinite solutions
86.	No solution (the two equations represent parallel lines so they do not intersect at any point).
87.	Infinite solutions (the two equations represent the same line so they intersect at infinitely many points).
88.	When you substitute an equation into itself, you will find the point where that line intersects a line exactly like itself. If two lines are the same, they intersect

	everywhere so your substitution yields an equation that is always true, like 0=0 or 4=4 or 2.37=2.37, etc. The equation always has infinite solutions.
89.	$h = 10, R = -27$
90.	$d = 50, h = 30$
91.	Equation 1: $7.50C + 10.50A = 6195$ Equation 2: $C + A = 680$ 315 children (365 adults)
92.	Equation 1: $p + q = 402$ Equation 2: $0.01p + 0.25q = 10.26$ 376 pennies, 26 quarters
93.	Equation 1: $5P + 2C = 9.75$ Equation 2: $4P + 5C = 13.75$ a. $1.75 per lb. (potatoes are $1.25 per lb.) b. $9.00; 3(1.25) + 3(1.75)$
94.	Equation 1: $B + C = 3,086$ Equation 2: $60B + 24C = 147,000$ a. 2,026 boxes b. 25,440 lbs.
95.	a. 16,514 pounds b. 35
96.	75 minutes; solve $150 + 10m = 12m$
97.	Equation 1: $2L + 2W = 36$ Equation 2: $L = 2W + 3$ width: 5 inches; length: 13 inches
98.	Elaine: $G = 12,500 - 30m$ Doris: $G = 14,000 - 45m$ a. Doris's pool contains 1,050 more gallons of water after 30 minutes b. 100 minutes (1 hour, 40 minutes)
99.	At 8:26am (after 26 minutes) Blue tank: $W = 1200 - 20m$ Red tank: $W = 160 + 20m$ Solve: $1200 - 20m = 160 + 20m$
100.	a. 4:28pm (1 hr. and 28 min. after 3pm) solve: $600 + 500h = 1,920 - 400h$; $h = 1$ and 7/15, or 1hr. and 28 min. b. 500 mph and 400 mph c. The slower plane is flying toward Seattle because its distance is decreasing.
101.	 a.

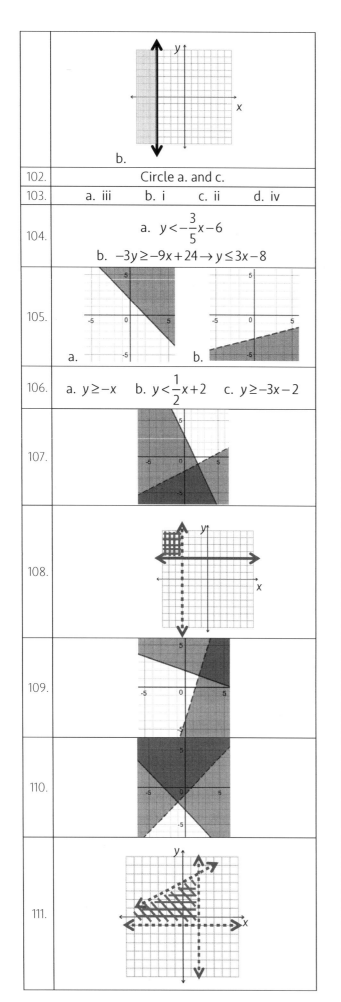

	b.
102.	Circle a. and c.
103.	a. iii　　b. i　　c. ii　　d. iv
104.	a. $y < -\dfrac{3}{5}x - 6$ b. $-3y \ge -9x + 24 \rightarrow y \le 3x - 8$
105.	a.　　　　　　b.
106.	a. $y \ge -x$　　b. $y < \dfrac{1}{2}x + 2$　　c. $y \ge -3x - 2$
107.	
108.	
109.	
110.	
111.	

112.	$\text{Area} = \dfrac{1}{2}(6)(12) = 36 \text{ units}^2$
113.	49, 64, 81, 100, 121, 144, 169, 196, 225
114.	125, 216, 343, 512
115.	$\dfrac{1}{4},\ -\dfrac{1}{8},\ \dfrac{1}{16},\ -\dfrac{1}{32}$
116.	$x = -\dfrac{1}{2}$
117.	a. $\dfrac{8x}{5y^5}$　　b. $\dfrac{1}{2^6}$ or $\dfrac{1}{64}$　　c. $\dfrac{7}{p}$　　d. $\dfrac{x^4}{9}$
118.	Area = 48 square units base = 12 units; height = 8 units
119.	a.　　　　　　b.
120.	$y = \dfrac{3}{5}x$
121.	Less than \$200,000 (\$198,000 to be exact). When the price drops by 10%, it is smaller than the original value. When the price then rises by 10%, it rises by 10% of a value that is less than \$200,000 so the price will not rise back to \$200,000 again.
122.	a. $\dfrac{48y}{72y^2} \cdot \dfrac{3y}{1} \rightarrow \dfrac{144y^2}{72y^2} \rightarrow 2$ b. $\dfrac{6x}{11} \cdot \dfrac{33}{48x^2} \rightarrow \dfrac{6x}{1} \cdot \dfrac{3}{48x^2} \rightarrow \dfrac{1}{1} \cdot \dfrac{3}{8x} \rightarrow \dfrac{3}{8x}$
123.	a. $\dfrac{2 \cdot 3}{7 \cdot 3} + \dfrac{2 \cdot 7}{3 \cdot 7} \rightarrow \dfrac{6}{21} + \dfrac{14}{21} \rightarrow \dfrac{20}{21}$ b. $\dfrac{2x \cdot 3}{4 \cdot 3} - \dfrac{7x \cdot 2}{6 \cdot 2} \rightarrow \dfrac{6x}{12} - \dfrac{14x}{12} \rightarrow -\dfrac{8x}{12} \rightarrow -\dfrac{2x}{3}$
124.	a. $\dfrac{x^2 - 4}{x - 2} \rightarrow \dfrac{(x+2)(x-2)}{x-2} \rightarrow x + 2$ b. $\dfrac{-2x - 6}{x + 3} \rightarrow \dfrac{-2(x+3)}{x+3} \rightarrow -2$
125.	a. 5　　b. 9　　c. $\dfrac{1}{2}$　　d. $\dfrac{6}{7}$